AIRLINE SAFETY IS A MYTH

AIRLINE SAFETY IS A MYTH

Capt. Vernon W. Lowell

BARTHOLOMEW HOUSE
Publishers

BARTHOLOMEW HOUSE

First Printing . . . . . March 1967

*Library of Congress
Catalog Card Number:
67-17140*

Photo Credits:

    *Acme Newspictures
Air Line Pilots Association
Boeing
Federal Aviation Agency
Metro News
UPI
Wide World*

Manufactured in the U.S.A.

CONTENTS

Acknowledgments

Air safety has been percolating in my mind for a long time. Nearly two years ago, I organized my efforts and began to write this book.

Many persons assisted me in different ways. Captain Alford D. Heath of TWA was my right arm. Without the able assistance of Tom Basnight, Director, Regulatory Matters, Air Line Pilots Association, this book would not have been truly complete. Mr. H. O. Van Zandt, Bachelor of electrical engineering, MS in mathematics, and an advanced student of mathematical statistics, helped in the development of much research material. I owe particular thanks to Bill Roach, a friend whose early interest inspired me in this effort.

Other persons made contributions that ranged from discussions of the safety issues to the submission of written material. I should like to express my thanks to all of them, and apologize to anyone who is inadvertently omitted from the list: Ingrid Abrahamsen, Gene Banning, Joe Bartling, Richard Beck, Robert D. Buck, Herb Broderick, Charles Buckley, John Carroll, Harry Clarke, George E. Drew, Irving Dale, Stan Doepke, Bob Early, Lt. Eric Fields, P. Lowell Fields, Rich Fluornoy, Ruby Garrett, John L. Graham, Ivan Levine, Julie Lowell, William Merrigan, William Murphy, Dave W. Richwine, M. G. Smith, Paul Townsend, R. W. VanEtten, Jim W. Walker, George White.

INTRODUCTION

With over a half million miles of safe and comfortable commercial air travel to my credit, I feel indebted to those who have made such service possible—the superb pilots and their crews, the designers and builders of the marvelous aircraft, the unsung heroes whose efficient maintenance "keeps 'em flying," the air controllers and other public servants whose lives are dedicated to safe flying, and the airlines themselves whose capital investment and far-sighted management brought together all these services to my benefit.

All of this is not to say that I have not had my moments of apprehension, said my prayers, and breathed my share of sighs of relief as a commercial air traveler. And the thought lingers that, while I was "lucky" and my number wasn't "up," perhaps something more might have been done to prevent or at least minimize a dangerous situation. However, to be fair about it, I would have to admit that I have had equally tense times in buses, taxicabs, trains, subways, and, indeed, my own automobile.

With our population explosion, we are witnessing a transportation explosion of even greater magnitude. According to Civil Aeronautics Board estimates, our domestic airlines last year carried 110 million passengers, and the prediction is made that by 1975 this number will be increased threefold. One thousand new aircraft, costing $7 billion, will be required within the next five years just to handle the increased passengers. By 1980 the average airliner will have 180 seats—double the average today. Needless to say, the problems of airport and air corridor congestion will worsen—not only for domestic flights but for overseas travel, including especially the North Atlantic.

An opportunity to learn first-hand about the problems of flying safety, deficiencies in present service and prospects for the future, along with knowledgeable and constructive suggestions, is presented in this book by Captain Vernon W. Lowell, a command pilot with Trans World Airlines for over 22 of his 28 years of airline piloting. He draws on his over five million miles of flying and his close work with the Airline Pilots Association to give the reader actual case histories to make meaningful his comments and criticisms. And one is left with the impression that preventive action can be taken by the airlines, the aircraft manufacturers, the various federal agencies having responsibility in this field, and by the Congress itself if need be. Indeed, he leaves with the Congress the question of whether it would not be more prudent to give a higher priority in federal spending to improve the design of present aircraft for added safety than to the development of still larger and faster transport aircraft which themselves do not incorporate needed safety design improvements.

This book merits careful and thoughtful reading by all who fly, whether by commercial, military, or private aircraft, by Members of Congress, interested federal agencies, and the airlines and aircraft manufacturing industries, and by all who are interested in safe transportation.

Jack Miller
U.S. Senator (Iowa)

FOREWORD

This book is good reading. Captain Lowell has condensed a surprising reservoir of technical knowledge and research into a document which contains information of value for everyone from aviation's high officials to the prospective passenger contemplating his first flight. The simplified catalogue and analysis of specific airports across the country should help bring the safety problem "close to home" for many readers. His eye-witness accounts of man and machine in the realm of flight have been carefully selected to illustrate each problem he identifies and each safety improvement he is crusading for.

Captain Lowell must be commended for his selfless and sincere effort to highlight hazards in aviation. This report is particularly unique when viewed against the fact that Vernon Lowell is presently employed as an airline captain. The succeeding pages are not the accusations of a "fired" pilot, but are the convictions of a man who is actively engaged in the business of air transportation. I do not agree with all of Captain Lowell's conclusions; however, the differences which we have may be due to the location of the observer, rather than the activity that is viewed.

The federal government investigates aircraft accidents, and the handful of men who accomplish that task are dedicated to aviation safety. This group, like Captain Lowell, can only report the facts of aircraft accidents and recommend changes to prevent the recurrence of similar accidents. Many of the safety deficiencies described by Captain Lowell have been the subject of accident reports and recommendations, but all too often those recommendations were not implemented due to "high expense" or have been permanently buried in the "committee appointed to study the problem." Washington is a town filled with monuments, and I have yet to see one dedicated to the accomplishments of a committee. As to expense—loss of business, destruction of expensive aircraft and the incalculable value of an eye, a limb or a life are a few of the costs of aircraft accidents which should be measured against the "expense" of improved safety.

In early fall of 1961, I served as the Federal Aviation Agency's attorney at the accident hearing in Denver, Colorado, where it was determined that asymmetric reverse thrust on a jet transport was a significant factor in the probable cause of that accident. Captain Lowell's crash, due to similar causes years later, emphasizes that the aviation industry must implement known improvements which will prevent the recurrence of similar accidents in the future.

Donald W. Madole, Esq.
Washington, D.C.

Donald W. Madole's background combines aviation and law. He was educated as an attorney, naval aviator and commercial pilot. He has served as a trial attorney for the FAA, Chief of Hearing and Reports Division—CAB, Member of the U.S. Delegation to ICAO, airline attorney, and a lecturer to the National Aircraft Accident Investigation School. He is the recipient of several performance and achievement awards for his activities.

PREFACE

When you buy your next airline ticket, take this book along on your trip and give air safety some thought.

This exposé of biased accident findings, marginally safe conditions in our planes, at our airports, and in our federal regulations was long overdue. It took considerable courage for a command pilot employed by a major airline to allow the public this candid view . . . but in aviation's inner circles, Vern Lowell is known for his deep concern on safety matters even more than for his fine flying record of a quarter of a century and five million piloting miles.

THE MYTH OF AIRLINE SAFETY is written from the heart—and from the brain. Lowell is competently backed up by authorities in all appropriate areas: airline operations, engineering, statistics, governmental operations, and many others.

The book delivers the mail. The average reader will be able to understand it only too well, and make his own determinations about unsafe runways in his own home-town airport, the perverse logic of "noise abatement" at the expense of safety, controversy over governmental accident investigations, the airlines' glamour-vs-safety situation, and the aircraft manufacturers' cost-vs-safety situation.

In my personal opinion, the letter from Captain Gale C. Kehmeier, only surviving captain of four fatal Boeing 727 accidents within six months, is one of the most extraordinary documents ever to be published in the jet age.

Although the book is an exposé, it is written for a humanitarian cause. Lowell has not said that flying is dangerous, he has said that it is not safe . . . *enough*. And it is *not* getting any safer year by year! (And if you thought that airliners are safer than automobiles, your illusions will be blown sky-high by his revealing job on "statistics.")

The main thing is, he has suggested remedies for the many ills he exposes. Perhaps the most significant remedy concerns the use of a true-adversary proceeding (a courtroom-type approach) for determinations of the probable causes of accidents.

In his book, Lowell has finally put the issue squarely before his readers, requesting them to join him in his crusade for air safety by appealing to their Senators and Representatives to sponsor the urgently needed legislation in Congress.

I urge everyone to read this book ... and to join Captain Lowell in his crusade for air safety!

Nino Ciancetta, Chairman
Air Safety, Region 1
Air Line Pilots Association

AIRLINE SAFETY IS A MYTH

I

THIS IS YOUR CAPTAIN SPEAKING

Let me introduce myself just as I do several times weekly, and have done for many years, from the flight deck: This is Captain Lowell speaking.

For more than twenty-two years I have been a command pilot for one of the world's largest airlines—and in my opinion the very best—TWA. I fly the international route over the Atlantic, and am assigned, as I write these pages, to the New York-Paris-Rome run.

I have earned my living as an airline pilot for twenty-five years. I attended commercial aviation schools in Maine and Massachusetts, and first flew solo in a single-engine open-cockpit Fleet biplane. Since then I believe I've flown virtually every type of commercial airliner and thus took part in the revolutionary transition to the Jet Age.

During World War II, I flew as a civilian pilot for the Air Transport Command of the U.S. Army Air Corps to just about every theatre of war.

The first three million miles in the air as a command pilot I logged carefully, but later the mileage record-keeping became cumbersome. Completing my credentials in brief, I have flown, as a pilot, over five million miles, spent more than twenty thousand hours in the air, and been responsible for a large number of very expensive, technically sophisticated airplanes ... and for the safety of my passengers and crew. Like any experienced command pilot, I've taken these responsibilities seriously.

I am also a family man, and enjoy such mortal pleasures as golf (I'm an avid participant and feel the usual golfer's frustration when my game is off) and a good steak dinner. I've been active in diverse activities within aviation and also outside. I have held supervisory positions and instructed pilots. For more than twelve years I was active with the Air Line Pilots Association in many areas, including the problems of flight safety.

My outside activities include the building business, among others. I served as an officer in the organization and initial development of the Old Westbury Golf and Country Club on the former Whitney estate on Long Island. I've been a director of the Brookville Country Club, also on Long Island, for seven years and served as president for the past three years. I'm on the board of directors of the *Long Island Commercial Review*.

But safety has always been my business. I've always been conscientious about my company's annual training, which includes classes in the handling of emergencies, and about keeping abreast in every way of the many technological changes in aviation—one of the fastest moving and developing industries on earth.

This means continual study—and no self-respecting pilot ignores it.

Like other pilots, I've always shuddered at an accident that takes human lives. I've made it a habit to read everything available on a crash, including the official reports published by the Civil Aeronautics Board, the government agency charged with the investigation of accidents.

For many years, however, I shared the feeling of so many of my fellow pilots: somebody else crashed, but it wouldn't happen to me. You can't fly an airplane successfully with a fixation on crashes, any more than you can sit behind the wheel of an automobile scared. The tension alone would make any man inefficient.

Then it happened. In Rome, on November 23rd, 1964, a Boeing 707 crashed on take-off, and of the total of seventy-three passengers and crew members on board, fifty-one died. I was the pilot.

The experience itself was a nightmare, as was the exhaustive, lengthy investigation that followed. The fact that I was cleared, absolved of all blame, was a matter of personal gratification to me, of course, and salvaged both my professional pride and my career. But it wasn't enough. I had seen people die, among them helpless passengers and colleagues who were close friends. I had been in command.

The accident haunted me. My company, the U. S. Government and the official report of the commission appointed by the Italian Ministry of Transport and Civil Aviation, a report that ran hundreds of pages, held me blameless. But accidents may occur again—under similar or related circumstances. Most of the basic problems remain.

In the two years that have passed since that November and my only accident, I have spent countless hours of study and research on air safety, in talks with fellow pilots, airplane technicians, company executives, and personnel of the two United States Government agencies charged with supervision of air travel, the Civil Aeronautics Board and the Federal Aviation Agency. I've talked with flight deck crew members and with the cabin personnel who, under certain emergency conditions, have safety functions to perform. I've had discussions with ground crew maintenance people, air traffic controllers, and the always important pilot safety representatives, many of whom spend the greater portion of their free time pursuing safety.

I have devoted, and will continue to devote, maximum effort on every possible answer to the question: Is commercial flying safe? What are the weaknesses? What, specifically, can be done to make improvements? Now! And in the future! I'm no starry-eyed visionary. I'm a realist who wants practical solutions to practical problems.

17

There are many such problems, most of them unknown to the general public who ride as passengers in commercial airliners. Yet I strongly believe that an *informed* public has the power to reshape an industry, a nation itself, for the universal public good. That's democracy.

You and I, together, can do a great deal to prevent future air tragedies.

This book, then, is the opening salvo in a crusade for improved safety that can—and, I fervently hope, will—prevent the deaths of many human beings.

II

THE FATE OF FLIGHT 800

The day began like hundreds of others. I climbed out of bed and, before my eyes were really open, looked out of the window of my room in the Hotel Celtic at the Paris sky. The morning promised to be fair.

I had my usual breakfast of rolls and coffee, telling myself that, even after all this time, I'd never grown accustomed to French coffee. Later, at Orly Airport, I went to the operations office, made out my flight plan and completed my pre-flight briefing. The weather was good over the entire European continent, I was told, except for fog in the valleys of northern Italy.

Then I picked up TWA Flight 800, which had originated in Kansas City, Missouri, and took command of the Boeing 707. My second officer, William Churchill, flew the first leg of our flight, from Paris to Milan. We encountered some fog as we came down, but the landing was routine. I flew the next leg from Milan to Rome.

As soon as we landed I went through the usual procedures: dispatch office, flight plan for the next leg (to Athens), pre-flight briefing. The weather was still good, everything was normal and while the ground crew checked the airplane, I strolled over to the terminal building, where I had lunch with Bill Churchill and his wife, who was flying with us as a passenger, intending to accompany her husband to our final destination, Bombay.

We chatted about our families, and had a pleasant, relaxed lunch. None of us had premonitions of disaster, nor did it occur to us that anything out of the ordinary might happen.

Just before departure time I went out to my ship and took my usual slow walk around it, making what we call a visual check. Everything seemed in order, and I went on board. Instead of four men in the cockput, we were now going to be five: Marty Shepherd, the head of TWA's dispatching department for Europe, was going to ride down to Athens with us. He requested permission to sit in the second officer's seat, as he wanted to check some new en route radio facilities. I granted the permission.

First Officer Bill Slaughter was going to fly the leg from Rome to Athens. We went through our pre-flight check list to make certain everything was in order, and then reviewed the area departure procedure for Rome. No sooner had we completed it than the control tower gave us a traffic clearance to start our engines and taxi out to the runway.

The airplane is taxied from the left side because only the captain has a steerable nose wheel (though all other controls are duplicated on the co-pilot's side). The normal procedure when the co-pilot is flying from the right side, as Bill Slaughter was going to do, is for the captain to steer the ship onto the runway and control its direction until a speed of eighty knots is reached, at which time he turns the airplane completely over to the co-pilot.

Traffic control gave us our clearance during the taxi run, which meant we were set for immediate take-off, so we didn't pause at the end of the runway. We completed our "before take-off" check list, and Slaughter assumed all of the flight and power controls except the nose-wheel steering. When we reached eighty knots, I told Slaughter we were at the prescribed speed and I took my hand from the nose-wheel control. This meant he would now control the direction of the airplane with the rudder.

At almost precisely this same instant, the main power indication instrument on the number 4 engine suddenly dropped to zero, or near zero. The members of my crew, following regulations to the letter, called this information to me. Two seconds later our trouble literally doubled: a reverse thrust light came on, indicating a malfunction in the number 2 engine.

We were accelerating very rapidly, and there was no time to evaluate these two mechanical failure indications. We had reached a speed of over one hundred miles per hour, and I was triggered instantly into assuming command of the airplane. An experienced pilot's mind works very rapidly under emergency conditions, and I decided at once—far more rapidly than it takes to tell—to abort the take-off.

I placed my hands on the thrust levers, and at the same moment my first officer, knowing precisely what to do under such circumstances, removed his hands. Without hesitation, I took several steps: I closed the thrust levers, which brings all engines back to idling power; I activated the speed brakes and the foot-wheel brakes, at the same time placing my hands on the reverse thrust levers and moving these controls into the reverse thrust range.

Complicated? Not really, to a pilot. In an aborted take-off, as well as in the normal procedure for halting after a landing, there are three means of bringing an airplane to a stop, all three usually used at the same time. One is the wheel brakes, the second the speed brakes, and the third a system of reversing the powerful jet thrust.

We were traveling down the center of the runway, and as I started the aborting procedures, the aircraft veered, or yawed, very sharply to right, almost driving the ship off the runway. A crew member shouted to me that the tires on the right rear trucks had blown. This followed a procedure approved by the FAA. The principle involved is that crew members can help alert the captain to abnormalities in take-off or landing.

21

AIRLINE SAFETY IS A MYTH

Although I did not completely accept this information as absolute fact, (we subsequently discovered that the crew member was mistaken; the tires had not blown) I was having a severe directional control problem, and released the brakes on the right side of the airplane.

Directly ahead of us, on both sides of the runway, we could see construction men working with heavy equipment. The last two thousand feet of the runway had been closed for this purpose. A heavy steamroller was moving from left to right, directly across my path, and I tried desperately to steer—or veer—to the left to avoid hitting it.

I failed. . . .

Number 4, the outboard right engine, struck the roller with great force and knocked it over. Approximately eight hundred feet beyond the roller, I finally succeeded in bringing my ship to a halt. Except for the number 4 engine, the airplane had not suffered any great damage.

But there was simply no time to congratulate ourselves on a narrow escape; just as I was "cleaning up" the airplane, that is, performing certain duties required after a landing roll, my first officer called to me that we had a fire on the right side.

I immediately cut all the engines, and activated the anti-fire controls. (Three simple steps are involved. First the captain moves four levers which shut off the engines. Then he pulls four fire control handles which shut off the fuel supply and hydraulic oil supply, disconnect the generator and arm the fire extinguisher system. Finally he presses a button which discharges a chemical that extinguishes the flames. These are normal safety measures. I'll have more to say about them later, too).

No sooner had I taken these three steps—or perhaps it happened more or less simultaneously—when there was a violent explosion that rocked the airplane. As of that instant, and from then on, we—my passengers, my crew and I—descended into the deepest pit of hell.

My second officer and flight engineer had already left the cockpit and were back at the front passenger door. The pursers were trying to put an emergency escape chute into operation. These chutes are activated by compressed gas and are somewhat similar to slides found in children's playgrounds.

The chute was tangled and had dropped to the floor backwards, and the crew were struggling to straighten it out. (I'll have a great deal to say about chutes subsequently.)

There was nothing more I could do in the cockpit, so I started back toward the cabin to help in the evacuation of the airplane, but I could see that the aisle was blocked. The passengers were surging toward the forward door of the cabin. The aisle was so choked that none of them could get out that way.

I ordered the crew to evacuate the aircraft. Then I opened my left side window, threw the escape rope out and climbed down it, intending to make my way as rapidly as I could to the bottom of the forward chute so I could speed the evacuation of the passengers from that end.

As I hit the ground, however, I saw a sea of fire directly under the entire airplane including the forward passenger entrance. One of the fuel tanks had been ruptured by the explosion, and fuel had been spilled in large puddles. It was at its worst directly under the passenger door, making it impossible for people to escape that way.

In a recklessness born of desperation, people were jumping from the airplane into the inferno below. Never have I seen anything as horrifying.

Most of what happened thereafter is a blur in my mind, and time lost all meaning. But some incidents stand out clearly in my memory, and I shall never forget them. One man was standing on the grass, dazed, his clothes on fire. I pushed him to the ground and managed to put out the flames by rolling him back and forth.

Warren Lowery, the flight engineer, was one of those who jumped into the inferno. The second officer had managed to extinguish the flames that enveloped him, but his clothes were oil-soaked and caught fire again. Working together, we managed to tear off his trousers and shirt, and for the moment, at least, he seemed relatively safe.

The very worst of the nightmare was yet to come. One of the passengers who jumped to the ground had become a human torch. Even his hair was flaming, and his wild screams still echo in my ears. As he staggered from the wreckage I ran to him, ripping off my shirt to smother the flames.

He fell to one knee, so close to the intense heat of the burning airplane that it wasn't possible to put out the fire. I tried to drag him away. I've always kept in good physical condition, partly for professional reasons, partly as a matter of personal pride, and I probably have greater strength than the average man. But I couldn't haul the poor passenger away from the airplane. He was still screaming, and his agony was so intense that it robbed him of his reason. Suddenly he collapsed onto the ground, and the combination of his inert weight, the fire and the blistering heat made it impossible for me to budge him. Eventually I had to abandon him, and I vaguely recall weeping.

There were several explosions, I can't recall how many, columns of black smoke made it difficult to breathe, and everywhere people were burning—and dying. At one point I remember shouting to Bill Churchill, who was busy helping other passengers around him, asking him if his wife had escaped. "My God," he shouted back, "she may still be in there."

I have no idea how long the few of us capable of assisting others worked to help the victims. It felt like an eternity before several fire trucks arrived and began to spray huge quantities of a fire-snuffing chemical on the burning wreck. So much happened within such a short time that I was surprised, later, when I learned that the trucks reached the scene of the fire within a very few minutes.

A number of ambulances roared up to the wreck, too, and began to remove the survivors. Among them was the flight engineer, who had suffered severe third-degree burns. As I helped him into the ambulance he managed to smile and assured me he was all right. Seventy-two hours later he died of his burns.

I searched everywhere for Bill Slaughter, but couldn't find him anywhere, and apparently no one had seen him. It was the next day, I believe, before I finally discovered that he had jumped from the right window of the cockpit, landing directly in the inferno. He broke his hip in the jump, rendering himself incapable of getting away from the fire.

I refused to leave the scene until the firemen and police had everything under control and had removed all of the injured. Bill Churchill stayed with me, working, and still knowing nothing of his wife's fate. He could only hope she had escaped and had been one of the passengers taken to a hospital by ambulance.

About an hour after the accident, Churchill and I were driven to the first aid station at the terminal. Only then did I realize that I had been burned and injured also. I had hurt my left foot while climbing out of the window, and had broken a finger on my right hand, apparently while climbing down the rope. I had also suffered burns on my arms and hands when helping passengers and crew members who had been on fire. But my injuries were minor.

Both of my flight pursers had suffered bad burns, and died while under hospital treatment. In all, there had been nine hostesses on board the airplane, most of them as passengers. Five had escaped alive, and were taken to the hospital, where two subsequently died.

While we were waiting in the first aid station, an airport policeman was taking names, apparently for identification purposes, and when he learned that I had been the captain he immediately contacted the chief of police who came to the first aid station and convened a board of inquiry. The police insisted that I give them a statement, which I dutifully did, and after informing me that this was an initial phase of their investigation, Churchill and I were driven to the San Eugenio Hospital.

Here, Bill continued to search frantically, but in vain, for his wife. Not until then, I think, did he finally abandon hope for her survival. The tragic irony is that Bill Churchill had been kneeling, assisting in straightening out the chute and protected by the food service bar at the front of the first class compartment, at the time of the explosion, no more than twenty feet from where his wife was sitting. Had he not been protected by this obstruction to the blast, it is doubtful that he would have survived.

The ensuing details are hazy in my memory. By now, shock was beginning to take its toll. I do recall being taken to a private room where police were posted outside the door, ostensibly to keep unwanted persons from entering, and after my burns were treated, three Americans were allowed to enter the room, after some consultation with the police: First, a fellow TWA pilot, Dick Beck; later a former TWA pilot, Don Terry, who at the time was an inspector for the Federal Aviation Agency based in Rome; and with him was Najeeb E. Halaby, then Administrator of the Federal Aviation Agency, who happened to be in Rome on other business.

The hospital staff continued to look me over while I was talking to these gentlemen, and I was given an injection, and even during our discussion I could begin to feel the effects of this sedation. I gave them the bare facts of the accident candidly, and I recall at this time my suspicion that there had been an asymmetrical thrust problem with one of the engines on the left side. But I couldn't find out from a hospital bed. To make a long story somewhat less long, I made such a fuss that I was permitted to leave the hospital in mid-afternoon the following day after signing a release and assuming full responsibility for the state of my health.

I was driven out to the airport runway in a police car, still under police guard, and the charred wreckage was surrounded by a cordon of policemen. The moment I saw my tire tracks, I knew that the tires on the right landing gear had not blown. It had to be something else. Could reverse asymmetrical thrust alone have caused this? It seemed impossible. I recalled increasing the reverse thrust on my number 1 and number 2 (left-side) engines. I recalled applying maximum braking on my left wheels and, as I slowed down, left nose-wheel steering.

It was not easy for me to look at the twisted remains of the airplane, with bodies still on the ground nearby, and continue an analysis. And I doubted that anyone would ever be able to reconstruct a complete, accurate analysis.

Returning from the accident scene on the runway to the modernistic terminal building, I was met by representatives of the Italian Department of Justice. A board of inquiry was being convened on the spot under the chairmanship of the Procurator of Justice; he had three magistrates from his department, and two Italian Air Force officers to assist. Early in the evening, they started a questioning session.

This was my first brush with the Justinian Code. My normal reaction was to request legal and technical representation, and an Italian-English interpreter of my own choice. But the members of this board carefully examined a volume the very title of which ("Criminal Code") caused me misgivings, and respectfully informed me that I was not entitled to the representation. This information was conveyed to me through *their* interpreter. That evening session was to be the first of several sessions before these gentlemen, and I was never allowed to have a representative in the hearing room with me, although fellow pilots, company officials, and attorneys had gathered from various places in the world to do whatever they could to assist in the investigation.

After several hours of questioning, I was driven back to the Hilton hotel, and when the door of my room closed behind me, I was truly alone for the first time since the accident. This was to be the worst night of my life.

Small children, young hostesses, priests, entire families, and the wife of one of my good friends had lost their lives. The death toll was still mounting. Headlines in thick black type screamed at me from newspapers. I had been the captain. At this point I actually regretted having escaped from the airplane.

By the early morning hours, after intense introspection and

reappraisal of all my actions as captain, I knew that I could not have performed in any other way with the developments and information I had available during those forty-odd seconds from the start of the take-off to the catastrophe.

The next morning, I went before the Department of Justice board again. This time the hearings were held in Rome in the Palace of Justice.

I cooperated in every way and responded to interrogation as best memory could serve me, and in a few days it seemed a rapport existed which eased some of my apprehensions. I began to appreciate the depth and extent of the investigation these officials expected, and outside of the language barrier, little difficulty remained in getting the complete story told. Naturally, I was still concerned about analysis of the story, nor could I predict just what effect the investigation would have on a determination of probable cause of the accident. I continued to testify through the following Friday, which in total hours (including two evening sessions) amounted to some thirty hours of responding to incisive questioning. By the end of this time, I was certain that all the information in which the Department of Justice had shown an interest had been recorded. They then released me.

Now I was to testify before another group, an Italian commission appointed by the Air Ministry. This commission was charged with investigation of aircraft accidents in accordance with the International Civil Aviation Agreements. My own government was represented by the CAB and the FAA. It would serve no useful purpose here to discuss the details of this complex investigation or of my personal conflicts with the CAB representative (who made moves to block my return to Rome after this commission released me for a few days of rest in New York). Let it suffice that I was completely exonerated by the Italian Department of Justice and the Air Ministry's Commission, as well as my government and my own airline.

But that was not good enough for me. Fifty-one people died. For their sake, I pledged to do everything within my power to root out and eliminate as many causes of accidents as possible. And there are special areas in which vast and immediate improvements must be made.

The Official Report

The Italian commission did a magnificent job. Fifteen months after the accident it completed its report, which I consider highly professional, absolutely unbiased, and the type of scholarly report which can be understood. It will be a useful tool for those in aviation who are dedicated to raising the level of air safety.

I now take the privilege of bringing to you the significant "Conclusions," "Probable Causes," and "Recommendations" sections from the report (as translated).

Conclusions (Chapter 13 of the Commission Report)

1. The aircraft was cleared as airworthy.
2. The crew was properly qualified and certified.
3. The flight plan was filed regularly, and was completed.
4. The Commander operated correctly according to the book.
5. The yellow warning light for the reverse thrust system on the Boeing 707/331 provides inadequate information on the position of the shells; in this particular case, the light was out of adjustment.
6. The current manual procedures for take-off refer to and are valid only in the case of maneuvers performed personally by the pilot.
7. The manual does not consider an aborted take-off an emergency maneuver.
8. The acceleration rate of the aircraft was normal.
9. The decision to abort the take-off was made before reaching critical velocity.
10. The reverse system of the no. 2 engine malfunctioned, and therefore the engine continued to pro-

vide forward thrust, and this was the cause of the uneven thrust during the deceleration phase.

11. There is no doubt that the pilot correctly pushed all four reverse levers firmly into the interlock position.

12. Deceleration was slower than expected, and uneven as well.

13. The aircraft was subjected to severe and continuous yaw strain.

14. The aircraft had gone beyond the legal limit of the runway and subsequently collided (with its no. 4 engine) with a steamroller which was operating in a repair zone that had been authorized and publicized according to ICAO regulations.

15. Fuel spurted from the surge tank on the right wing, and this provided a means of ingress for the fire.

16. The fire alarm system was out of commission.

17. The explosions which occurred in a very brief interval after the aircraft had come to a stop were followed by a fire of major proportions.

18. The most violent explosion occurred in the central tank.

19. The wing emergency exits of the Boeing 707/331 are demonstrably difficult to reach and to open because the backs of the seats hinder access to them.

20. The evacuation slides have proved difficult to operate.

21. Fire-fighting and first-aid crews from two different stations took from about 3 to 5 minutes after the aircraft had come to a halt to get to the scene of the accident.

Probable Causes (Chapter 14 of the Commission Report)

1. Malfunction of the reverse thrust system in the no. 2 engine, which could not have been detected by the instruments aboard. The defect was a break

in a tube connection and a consequent lack of pressure in the pneumatic shell-activator system. This malfunction allowed the no. 2 engine to produce a forward thrust although the levers for all four engines were in reverse position.

2. A break in the fuel feed line to the no. 4 engine caused by the impact of the engine against the steamroller, and consequent combustion of the leaking fuel.

3. Faulty shuttle valve in the surge tank which allowed fuel to leak out of the scoop vent and the fire to penetrate the interior of the wing structure.

4. The presence of a volatile mixture of air and fuel, formed and built into explosive proportions inside the fuel tank. One touch of flame, and this mixture exploded.

Recommendations (Chapter 15 of the Commission Report)
(A) Operational Recommendations
1. Establish realistic certification and operating standards for take-offs handled by the co-pilot.

2. Include aborted take-off procedures among emergency operations for all purposes and under all conditions.

(B) Technical Recommendations
1. Install a system that will indicate the several positions of the reverse shells.

2. Require brakes on all connections with the pneumatic reverse system.

3. Devise a way to power the fire alarm system in parallel with every other source of electrical power aboard.

4. Continue the search for systems that will eliminate the danger of explosions in the fuel systems, and prevent outside fires from entering the wing structures through the air vents.

5. Improve the effectiveness of the drainage system for the surge tanks, so as to prevent accumulation of fuel.
6. Make the wing emergency exits more accessible; figure out a way to make the slides easier to get out, set up, and slide down.

Over two years have passed since the accident, and to my knowledge the FAA and the industry have not taken corrective action relative to these findings.

TRAGEDY'S LESSONS

The real "killer" in my Rome accident was fire and resulting explosions. By the time I was able to bring my airplane to a halt after striking the steamroller, the passengers had been given a bad scare and the crew members an unpleasant and busy few moments, but no one had been injured or killed. Number 4 engine had been damaged by the steamroller and, unknown to us in the cockpit, a fire was in progress. Within seconds, fuel tanks exploded and human lives were snuffed out.

Exploding Fuel Tanks

No single cause of injury or death to passengers is more serious than exploding fuel tanks and the ensuing blanketing of large areas by flaming liquids. It is the empty or partly filled tank that is potentially the most dangerous because the tank fumes are volatile.

A basic fact about jets: they burn vast quantities of fuel, and require tanks with enormous storage capacities. Yet it would not be efficient to carry extra thousands of pounds of fuel on all flights. Thus, a jet aircraft will have a heavier fuel load on a transatlantic crossing than on a flight from New York to Chicago, or from Rome to Athens, the route of my own Flight 800.

On most flights, therefore, one or more of the several fuel

tanks are completely or partially empty. Even if filled at the beginning of a flight, large amounts are burned while taking off and in the air, so there will be those completely or partially empty tanks as the flight nears its end.

Consequently, *some volatile fumes are present on almost every flight*. These fumes can be ignited through the vent system by a flame or spark. It may happen in mid-air, caused by lightning or static electricity; it may happen on the ground, during take-off or landing, caused by fire developing as the result of an accident.

Let me cite examples: On December 8th, 1963, a PAA jet blew up in the air over Elkton, Maryland. Eighty-three people lost their lives. It was later established that a tank containing residual JP-4 fuel had exploded as a result of lightning-induced ignition.

In 1959 a TWA Constellation flew near a thunderstorm area shortly after take-off from Milan, Italy. Either lightning or static electricity shot through a vent system and exploded a tank, causing the plane to crash and killing everyone on board.

In 1961 a UAL DC-8, encountering an asymmetrical thrust condition on landing, swerved and collided with a construction truck. The fuel system exploded. The overall similarity to my accident five years later is a bitter fact. In those five years, emergency exits had not been improved, nor was the asymmetrical thrust warning system corrected.

In my Rome accident, nobody had been injured up to the time the plane stopped. The explosions in the fume-filled tanks were the major contributing factor to the loss of fifty-one lives.

The potential escape time from the aircraft was drastically reduced, as the first explosion took place only twenty seconds after the airplane was stopped.

Everyone in the aviation industry is aware of the hazards caused by these fume-filled tanks, but, up to the time of the present writing, the problem is still with us.

One of the most controversial aspects of the problem is the

placing of fuel tanks in the fuselage, the center section of the airplane. Arguing this issue as far back as 1939, pilots maintained that fuel should not be placed in the same structural compartment as the passengers. Although pilots took a strong stand against placing fuel in the fuselage, the public demand for increased range and additional speed prevailed and the pilots had to agree to carry fuel in the vulnerable belly tanks since the wings were no longer large enough to store the fuel demanded by the thirsty jet engines.

Perhaps a brief quote from the official Italian Commission report on my Rome accident will indicate the gravity of the problem caused by explosions in empty or almost empty tanks: "Twenty seconds after the airplane came to a stop (according to data taken from the flight recorder and numerous witnesses) the most violent explosion took place . . . The violence of this explosion was so extreme as to cause the fatal injuries found on the twenty-nine bodies recovered from the wreckage of the aircraft. The type of injuries obviously traceable to the explosion were lacerations and contusion wounds, 18; amputations, 17; extensive incisions, 10; and fractures, chiefly to the legs, 18. Since the aircraft decelerated slowly to a stop, it was found that the only possible cause of such injuries must be the explosion."

Aeronautical science is sufficiently advanced so that fuel tanks *can* be made safe from explosion. Fumes can be chemically inerted, and flames and sparks can be snuffed out instantly by devices already developed.

Why aren't these—and other—safety devices being utilized on every airplane in commercial service?

On the other side of the fence, however, there are encouraging developments. TWA, acting completely on its own initiative, is retro-fitting present planes with a system that is designed to snuff out any flame or spark in the fuel vent system. Certainly this is an important step in the right direction.

Undoubtedly, at some future time the Federal Aviation Agency will require modifications of present jets and changes in future jets to reduce—perhaps to eliminate—the hazards caused by dangerous fume-filled tanks, but that day has not yet arrived.

JP-4 Fuel

JP-4 fuel, which was developed primarily for military operations, is more volatile than kerosene in the temperature range of our normal operations. It does have some desirable operating characteristics. For example, it is lighter and has a lower freezing point than other jet fuels. Since it performs just as efficiently, it was for some time used almost universally in commercial flying.

However, many pilots objected to the use of JP-4 fuel. (If only they had realized the full significance of the higher volatility factor and had objected more strongly, then JP-4 might have been discontinued at an earlier date.) One by one, all airlines have stopped using JP-4 fuel. Nevertheless, the FAA has still not rescinded its approval. In view of everyone else's capitulation to the facts, why won't the FAA change its position?

Emergency Escape from Airliners

Inadequate means of escape from a crashed or burning airliner is a major cause of fatalities during take-off or landing.

Approximately ninety percent of all airline accidents take place during take-off and landing. In the overwhelming majority of instances, loss of life is caused by fire and smoke inhalation rather than the force of impact.

The escape means provided in most airplanes are inadequate. Again, let me cite a few examples.

In the 1961 UAL DC-8 accident, sixteen of the one hundred twenty-two occupants of the airliner died. The airplane itself was intact: smoke and fire were the causes of death. In the tourist compartment of this airplane, one exit served eighty-one people . . .

On November 11th, 1965, in a United Airlines Boeing 727 accident, forty-three people out of a total of ninety-one on board died. All deaths were caused by fire rather than the impact.

One of the survivors, Ralph H. Dawson Jr., a former safety engineer, who had been employed by a major chemical company, had a number of observations which, he said, were based "on personal experience in scrambling out an emergency window." He said: "People should be thoroughly oriented to each plane on each flight. My close business associate died in the plane. He was sitting right across the aisle from me in row 17. He was a state champion in three sports, but he went by five exits to be caught by the smoke with twenty-nine others in the front of the plane. This shows the concentration needed to get the human mind to function properly in an emergency.

"In my own case, I remember during the preflight instruction in Denver, looking at the window exit at row 14 being nearest. After the crash, when I saw the fire behind me, I vividly recall focusing my eyes on that area and never took them off it until I dived head first onto the wing. Smoke obliterated the opening about the time of the escape."

According to the interview with Dawson (published in *Aviation Week & Space Technology* on April 4th, 1966) he further said that the Martin 404, an airplane carrying forty passengers, has eight exits, well distributed, while the Boeing 720, carrying one hundred and thirteen passengers, has only six exits, two of which are over the wing and partially blocked when seats are in their normal upright position.

Mr. Dawson is right. Two of the exits are indeed partly blocked when the seats are in their normal position. It is awkward, if not actually difficult, to reach them quickly.

To go on. This observer noted that, because of greater seating concentrations on a jet, people are unable to move around as rapidly as in a piston transport. "It is good to have larger and more floor-level doors," he said, "but it is not good to have sardine-packed three-seat rows and narrow aisles which restrict movement to the better opening. If you look at a 727 exit design, you find five of the six exits concentrated in a six-row area of a twenty-one seat-row aircraft—can anyone sincerely tell me this is not conducive to a jamming situation?"

Dawson further said that the FAA's evacuation demonstration rule, requiring proof that an aircraft can be emptied of passengers and crew in two minutes, using fifty percent of available exits, is "unrealistic." This is because those who take part in the test demonstrations know they are being required to evacuate an airplane; no actual emergency exists; there is a courtesy on the part of the evacuees which would not be present in a genuine emergency; there are no allowances made for the reactions of the passengers who are shocked or stunned; and there is no fire to create the actual panic that makes passengers stampede. Most of those who take part in these demonstrations are airline employees. They are not only familiar with the aircraft itself, but they know precisely what is going to happen. They know they are merely taking part in a test, so they have nothing to fear. The escape procedures are carefully reviewed for them by cabin personnel—hostesses and pursers. There are no test requirements for elderly people on board, no babies, no crippled or otherwise handicapped persons. Nor are there foreigners (of whatever nationality) who do not understand the language or languages spoken by cabin personnel.

Dawson has also suggested better emergency lighting and exit signs, and a special grillwork on the floor near the exits to give passengers blinded by smoke an opportunity to feel their way toward the doors or windows that could lead to safety.

Most of his suggestions are good, but the problem must be attacked in other ways also.

First, the passengers should be given maximum protection from explosions and fires to reduce those causes of panic and stampede. The passenger cabin should be made as safe as possible. If this means, for example, moving the fuel tanks away from the passenger cabin, which could require a major change in the design of the aircraft, then the change should be made regardless

38

of expense. The safety of the passengers must be the primary concern of the aircraft designer and manufacturer, the airliner company and the crew of the ship itself.

Second, and equally important, emergency escape means from airplanes must be simplified and improved. Generally speaking, the rear of an airplane is the safest part of the ship in the event of an accident. Usually it is located at the most distant point from an impact force, and from the areas that are the first to catch fire.

I know of no airplane flying today that has adequate means of escape from the rear. Take the British-built BAC 111. A pilot friend of mine, seated in the last row of the tourist section of one, was surprised when the hostess pointed out the emergency exits—only two in the compartment, and located far forward. He later checked for an exit in the rear of the airplane but was unable to locate it, or any sign indicating that one existed. If the pilot couldn't locate the exit then, how could the average passenger locate it in time of emergency?

Let me return for a moment or two to the chutes used on the jets. And by way of a preamble, let me point out that the techniques of making these chutes operational depend on the type of chute being used. There are several versions, and the procedures for each differ. Thus, the hostess whose duty it is to make the chutes operational must know and remember which type is installed, even though each week she may fly in planes using different types.

Theoretically, she can do the job in ten seconds. She performs five or six operations (each simple enough in itself but like a Rube Goldberg invention when combined)—and she performs perfectly . . . in tests. Practice has made her smooth and efficient.

But in a test, the young woman is not subjected to emotional pressures. She is not blinded by smoke or singed by fire. She is not harassed by passengers who may have become fear-infected by an emergency.

Consider, next, the escapes. These emergency exits should be

39

so easy to use that even the totally inexperienced air traveler can use them. Safeguards should be built in so that an irrational passenger could *not* use them at will during take-off, landing, or in flight, to the harm of himself or others.

There should be *more* exits. And they should be *located* at points as far as possible from the engine and the fuel tanks, where the danger of fire is the greatest. And they should become operational *automatically* under certain conditions, too.

There are numerous other steps that might be taken to facilitate escape from a burning airplane. For example, there might be an automatic tape recorder to instruct passengers precisely where the exits are located, and so forth. This recorder could be installed in such a way that it would operate automatically in the event that the captain and the members of his cockpit crew were incapacitated.

I am pleading here for greater imagination and ingenuity in safety designs.

Let's say a hostess looks out of a window and sees that the airplane is on fire. At present, she and the other cabin personnel must evaluate the situation and go through a complicated procedure to activate *each* emergency chute. The four simplest escape exits are removable panels. Unfortunately, they are located over the wings, near the engines and fuel tanks, the area where most fires originate.

While it may not be easy to design, what is needed is a basic device similar to the tailgate of a horse van. In brief, ramps of some kind would fall to the ground, on an angle, and the passengers could walk quickly and easily from the airplane in the event of an emergency. It would be designed, let me reemphasize, so it could not be operated while the ship is in the air. It would be designed, too, so that it could be made operational from both the cockpit and the passengers' compartment.

Still other areas need to be explored. An airplane might be equipped, for instance, with individual or automatic chemical spray guns to extinguish fires.

40

I am concerned by the immediate future. Still larger jets than those now in use have been ordered by the major airlines, at great expense. Airplanes like the Boeing 747 and the Lockheed C-5A will carry between four hundred and five hundred persons or up to 900 troops, depending on the seating arrangements. *Immediate* steps must be taken to provide adequate emergency escape exit systems in the original design of the aircraft. The complicated chutes and slides in use today have proven tragically inadequate to the job of saving lives in emergencies. Better devices are essential.

The supersonic airplane is just around the corner. At the time of writing, a special commission appointed by the President of the United States has reported that it will cost approximately four and one-half billion dollars to build, test and make operational the first ship. I can only hope that as much ingenuity and care will go into the designing of their emergency escape features as their size and speed. Passengers simply cannot continue to travel in fire traps from which not even the great magician, Houdini, could have escaped.

Emergency and Routine Crew Training

Vast amounts of time and effort, and huge sums of money, are spent in the training of airplane crew members for all these emergencies. A substantial portion of the Federal Aviation Agency's proficiency checks deal with emergency procedures.

When the pilot takes his classroom training, then his flight simulator training, and finally his training in the air, he memorizes these procedures and learns to perform them in a routine manner. Sounds good, doesn't it?

But the very word "emergency" implies the unexpected. Emergencies don't follow routines. Each is a new and critical experience.

Training programs should be designed not only to familiarize each individual with the emergency equipment but also to develop initiative and resourcefulness. Too much reliance on procedures that are robot-automatic can aggravate an already serious situation.

Now let me return to an earlier-mentioned procedure that has long worried pilots. You'll recall that in my Rome accident, a member of my crew called out to me that the right rear tires had blown. He was acting in accordance with a requirement that any crew member should call to the captain any malfunction.

In my accident, this information, although given in all urgent good faith, was erroneous. I am not saying that the crash with the steamroller at the end of the runway could have been averted if the tire report hadn't been given to me. I do say, however, that such shouted advice is distracting. It can definitely confuse your thought processes. I dislike the regulation. Indeed I feel very strongly that it *increases* the hazards on both take-off and landing, just at the time when a pilot needs to concentrate his complete attention on his own intricate tasks.

Before leaving the subject of training and procedures, a word about co-pilots. In theory, their training is adequate. In practice, it is not. For example, few companies give co-pilots sufficient training in actually flying jet airplanes, which is something the co-pilot might have to do, in an emergency. Human lives are precious, jet airplanes are expensive (the operational cost of the Boeing 707 is approximately $900 per hour) and airline companies should be required to raise their standards of co-pilot flight training and be less dependent on training during regular scheduled flights.

V-1: the Point of No Return

As we have already seen, the take-off and landing phases of a flight are by far the most hazardous. On a strictly mathematical basis, computed according to actual accidents, the government's official figures are startling. Comparing risks, a take-off and landing is equivalent to four hours of cruising flight. *A take-off or landing is approximately thirty times more hazardous than is cruising.*

The danger has not decreased with the advent of jets mainly because a jet airplane is far heavier than the conventional airplane, and takes off and lands at far higher speeds.

The Federal Aviation Agency has established a criterion for the take-off performance of a jet airplane, and pilots are required by law to abide by this regulation. And this is the point at which my fellow pilots and I part company with the FAA. V-1 (Velocity-1) is the supposed "decision speed" on a take-off. It is the "go" or "no-go" point. An airplane's V-1 on any single take-off depends on many factors, mainly its gross weight and the length of the runway. In brief, and without becoming too technical, there is no *one* V-1 speed. V-1 for each flight is calculated by using a variety of conditions and factors.

The rules were established, once again, under ideal test conditions which never exist in day-to-day flying. The regulations speak in terms of blacks and whites. But there are no blacks and no whites, only grays. Let's examine the situation in detail.

A test pilot (he is an employee of the aircraft manufacturer) who has had long practice in the precise maneuver he is about to perform and who is duly keyed up for the test run first takes off, using a runway marked off at a certain length, with a certain gross weight. Then on the next test, under the same conditions, he will abort the take-off.

He is attempting to prove a maximum capability without bad weather or other problems. The plane manufacturer will be gratified by these test performances. And regulations will be established from these tests of the V-1 criteria.

Every pilot is now expected to conform to these regulations, even though the conditions, which were so ideal in the test runs, may vary widely in actual operations.

A heavily loaded international jet eats up nearly two miles of runway from the time it begins its take-off run to the time it reaches an altitude of one hundred feet at a speed of two hundred miles per hour. During these sixty seconds of transition the captain must cope with any failures, such as mechanical or engine malfunction, tires flying apart and instrument failures. If he doesn't use up the runway or run afoul of these or other conditions, he manages to get his giant ship (which weighs about three hundred thousand pounds or more) safely into the air.

Yes, that one minute frequently feels like hours. The engines burn one thousand pounds of fuel during that brief span. And every captain feels that his "fuel" is being used up, too.

Now, let's go back to our test pilot, whose run determines the criteria for V-1. He flies a ship carefully prepared for his test. Its brakes, tires and so forth are perfect. His airplane has not just returned from a long run, and a short servicing. Nor has he picked it up at an airport during the middle of its run from one city to another. With his toes on the wheel brakes and his hands on the thrust levers, he knows the exact speed that the emergency will occur, and he aborts the take-off perfectly. Every step of his maneuver has been carefully rehearsed. He accomplishes his thrust reduction, activating his spoilers (speed brakes) and his wheel brakes at the same instant and proves the stopping capabilities.

How different are the actual working conditions on a regular flight! Your tires aren't brand new. Your brakes have not been adjusted for this take-off. Your take-off hasn't been plotted under ideal conditions. The runway concrete is still damp and slippery after an early morning rain. You hope, but don't know with absolute certainty that once you reach the go or no-go speed, your aircraft has the capability of continuing acceleration with one engine inoperative, and reaching a safe altitude, clearing all obstructions. You're taking off from a busy, crowded airport, not an open area with a very long runway.

The airline pilot, having computed his V-1 speed by using charts, and by taking into consideration such factors as his airplane's gross weight, the temperature, and so on, starts his take-off run by opening his thrust levers. As the airplane accelerates, he monitors his engines, at the same time keeping his aircraft on a straight course down the runway. The initial phase of the take-off is controlled by the nose-wheel steering mechanism, and as he gathers speed the directional control is maintained by the rudder, which he operates with his feet.

Let's assume that the decision speed for this particular airplane on this particular flight is one hundred and forty knots. He just reaches it, or, to make the illustration more emphatic, he reaches a speed of one hundred and forty-one knots. According to "the book," the regulations, he must now take off. But at this instant one of his engines fails or he has a fire warning, blown tire or other problem. He is so close to the decision speed that he knows, from his experience, that no matter what the regulations say, his airplane does not definitely have the capability of continuing to accelerate and get into the air and the pilot may not *want* to get into the air. A pilot abiding by this regulation may very well have serious problems. He may be forced to throw the rule book out of the window and abort the take-off.

He would then close the thrust levers with his right hand. At the same instant he presses his wheel brakes, very hard, with his feet. Then, with his right hand, he reaches over and pulls the speed brake lever, while simultaneously he continues to control the direction of the airplane either with his rudders or his brakes.

If he wants to use the reverse thrust of his engines, he faces a problem. If he has lost one of his engines, his reverse thrust would be asymmetrical. Therefore, in order to balance the braking action of the engines, he would be able to use only two of them, either his two inboard or two outboard engines.

Then, as he slows down, he takes his left hand from the control column and puts it on the nose-wheel steering mechanism to assist in the directional control of the airplane during the deceleration period. If he performs all these functions as he should, he has taken the safest action possible, nevertheless he is in trouble for violating a regulation.

Let's take an even more graphic example. The pilot has passed his V-1 of 140 knots. His tires have blown. The chances are great that flying chunks of rubber will cause other damage. Acceleration stops and he knows he cannot take off, even though he has passed V-1. He also knows that, even if he succeeds in taking off, he will have trouble retracting the landing gear, so the plane may never be capable of accelerating to cruising speed. Also, there is the problem of landing at the destination.

Again, he does what any man with common sense would do. He deliberately breaks the regulations and aborts the take-off.

In both examples, and I could cite countless others, the V-1 criteria in FAA regulations prove totally unrealistic.

The FAA has an answer to my arguments, of course. The captain always has what is known as "emergency authority." Under this authority he is empowered to discard regulations and follow the dictates of his own judgment. Fair enough, so far.

But if he makes the slightest error, may the Lord have mercy on him. He has used his own judgment and then slipped. The mistake may be very minor, causing no damage to his airplane and no harm to his passengers and crew. However, he has broken the rules.

Pilots are probably the most regulated people in the whole U. S. society. The hours of work and rate of pay are regulated under the Railway Labor Act. Their physical requirements, proficiency requirements and hours of rest are regulated by the FAA. In event of a goof or unfortunate accident they are ultimately regulated by a decision handed down by a CAB appeals procedure.

Since we are so regulated by government agencies I believe we are well qualified to show others the restrictive situations which surround the pilots.

Certainly the airlines are very much aware of the complex dangers created by take-off problems. Using one airline's training bulletin in advising pilots, "The decision to abort a take-off involves a thought process fraught with potentials for trouble. It necessitates a sudden reversal in plans from the inherent intent of the take-off maneuver and a shift in gears in the use of controls. There is not the slightest doubt that this factor causes inordinate delays in execution of the abort procedure, and occasional omissions in the procedural steps."

The decision point is so critical that a new regulation was recently issued. If the co-pilot is making the take-off and something happens that requires an abort, the co-pilot—not the pilot—is required to perform the aborting procedures. They consider V-1 so critical that, should there be a delay of only a few seconds before the captain takes over, the airplane might easily go off the end of the runway.

This regulation itself creates a serious conflict. The captain is responsible, and is held responsible, for everything that takes place when his aircraft is operational. He is required to assume command of his airplane, and actually take over the controls whenever he deems it advisable or necessary. Yet this recent regulation prohibits him from doing his duty or assuming the command function that is legally his responsibility. This conflict adds one more hazard.

There are other factors that vary the decision point and create constant hazards on take-offs, among them runways made slippery not only by water, but snow or ice. There is always the possibility of tire failure, brake failure, uneven braking, mechanical failures, control failures. The list is endless.

The Italian Commission investigating my Rome accident recognized the many grave problems connected with the establishment of the V-1 decision speed, and made a formal request that the FAA, CAB or some other United States Government body conduct further flight tests for the purpose of establishing more realistic criteria. This request was denied.

And so a substitute test was conducted in a *flight simulator* (about as *similar* to an actual jet as Grandma Moses was to Brigitte Bardot) in a building in Kansas City, Missouri, on February 19th, 1965. Present were representatives of the CAB and FAA, the Italian Commission, TWA, Boeing, the Air Line Pilots Association and the flight engineers' organization. The

47

flight condition explored were intended to validate time and motion studies. Speed and distance profiles were not included.

The reaction times of pilots performing various functions connected with the abort procedures were considered realistic, although the preamble of the report subsequently issued by the CAB stated that these tests should not be interpreted as producing deceleration forces or speed overrun values which were indicative of the values that would have resulted had an actual airplane been used under the same conditions. Why was this noted in the preamble? Would the speed overrun values have proved embarrassing?

There were no surprise elements in the flight simulator tests. The pilots "flying" the tests knew precisely what was going to happen, and when.

These tests proved little, if anything, of value. An actual airplane carrying a simulated heavy load under conditions similar to those in a regular flight would have been worth infinitely more. *Why wasn't the real airplane used?* Was the cost of one government-owned airplane too much ... or would the test have shown the V-1 criteria to be as unrealistic as we know them to be? (The FAA insisted on using a real airplane when they reexamined my abort procedure—but was that for the sake of safety, or tidying their own records?)

There are still other potential dangers. The possibility of engine fire is present. In winter, there are problems with slush. On very hot summer days, pavements may become soft and delay acceleration. Brakes may drag. For any one of many reasons, engines may not produce their full power. Instead of losing one engine's power, two may conk out.

What is the basic point I am trying to make about V-1? It is simply this: the FAA regulations, although originally designed to enhance safety, fail to accomplish this goal. *On the contrary, they hamper safety.*

It is obvious to me, as I am sure it will be to the reader, that it is better for an airplane to go off the end of the runway onto rough ground at a speed of fifty or sixty miles per hour than for a pilot to obey the V-1 regulations to the letter, and fall out of the sky a mile or two from the end of the runway while traveling at a speed of one hundred fifty miles per hour, or thereabouts.

The effect of this regulation is to trap the pilot. He needs a realistic V-1 decision speed, but only as a guide to enable him to make a safe decision—without forcing him to fall back on his "emergency authority" and worry about the hindsighters.

If the pilot's company has enough faith in him to entrust the lives of a great many passengers and crew members to his care, not to mention a very expensive airplane, then the government should let him use his head, and without suspending over it the threat of punishment. So-called "emergency authority" becomes meaningless if he must cross every bureaucratic "t" and dot every bureaucratic "i."

I am not claiming that pilots are perfect. As a matter of fact, I'll have some observations on their weaknesses in a subsequent chapter. But they are sober, adult men, dedicated to their work. They are professionals who willingly assume their responsibilities and are aware of the weight of those responsibilities. If anyone thinks I am being overly dramatic about V-1 problems, let me issue a flat challenge to those who disagree with me:

1. Select a jet airplane at random, taking it from line flying without submitting it to a special maintenance check for engine thrust output, braking power, tire conditions or anything else. In other words, take an airplane that has, let's say, taken off from New York and has landed at O'Hare Airport in Chicago en route to Los Angeles. Or taken off from New York and landed at Orly, Paris.

2. Select a pilot. Make certain he's an experienced line captain, which means he'll probably have logged several million miles in the air.

3. *Don't* tell this pilot what is going to happen. Give him no idea of the nature of the test he'll be required to perform.

49

4. Take him to a test site that will, actually, provide the maximum safety conditions. It will be in a place where the climate is dry, the temperatures moderate. Make certain the runways he will use for his test are exceptionally long, much longer than those to be found in most airports that accommodate jets.

5. Perform an aborted take-off, after loading the airplane to its maximum weight. Be generous in judging your distances, and even under these circumstances, see if the pilot can bring the airplane to a halt before reaching the end of what would be a runway at any commercial airport.

He would not be able to halt the airplane before reaching that point. He would, theoretically, crash.

6. Go on to the next test. Have the pilot simulate an engine failure just beyond V-1 and see if he can get the ship safely into the air before reaching what would normally be the end of the pavement.

The test would finally prove the FAA's V-1 criteria completely unrealistic.

7. Perform still another test. Have the pilot perform the test outlined in step 5—on a *wet* runway. Well, I must be fair: I would not want a pilot even to try.

Let me emphasize that I have not been talking only about heavily loaded, large jet airliners that fly on intercontinental or other long-range flights. Everything I have said is equally true of the smaller jets that operate out of small airports with short runways. Whenever they are loaded to the maximum weight allowable for those runways, they are engaging in an extremely hazardous operation.

What can be done to improve the situation, to make take-offs safer? The solution is simple though expensive. It requires construction of longer runways or reduction of the allowable gross take-off weight on marginal-length runways.

Testing procedures are unrealistic.

IV

SAFETY PROBLEMS—AND PEOPLE

Jet airplanes are built, flown and maintained by people, and carry people as passengers. Therefore modern flying is subject to the human equation. One of the most serious of these is crew fatigue.

Fatigue
Because the destination airport is closed down by weather, let's say, the pilot diverts to an alternate. The weather now is not good at the second airport either, but it is better than that at the original destination. In any event, the pilot must make an instrument approach and landing in adverse weather.

The flight has been a long one, and he has been on duty for many hours. He has been working all day (or all night—anyone who has worked the "graveyard shift" knows this) and must now execute precise maneuvers that require alterness. But he is tired, his ability to focus sharply is reduced, and his mind operates more slowly. He has been working in a confined space, and has been subjected to constant high-frequency noise and vibrations.

Another big problem facing jet pilots and their cockpit crews is that the moisture content of the air is drastically reduced. Captains and their crews can become dehydrated, which causes fatigue. Oxygen intake has been reduced substantially below normal, and this, too, makes the pilot and his subordinates weary.

Landing operations, as such, will be discussed elsewhere in these pages, but it is obvious that the safety hazard is increased when a captain and his crew are tired: at a time when their energies are depleted and their ability to function is at a low ebb, a maximum effort is required of them.

The best way to overcome this problem is to provide on-board rest facilities for the pilot and his crew.

A directly related problem is that of the maximum flight time a pilot should work. The Federal Aviation Agency's regulations establishing crew flight time limitations are totally unrealistic. Therefore the pilots have been forced to demand more realistic flight-time regulations in their working contracts with the airline companies.

The FAA differentiates, for example, between international and domestic routes. The quarrel between the pilots and the industry is an old one. Inevitably, hard feelings have been caused on both sides.

There is no question in my mind that if we were to operate by the FAA limitations the accident rate would rise sharply! For example, FAA regulations limit a pilot to twelve hours of flight time in a given twenty-four hour period. There are no provisions made for a rest period during the 24 hours; in the absence of such provisions he may be on duty for the 24 hours while flying the twelve, and the cycle may be repeated immediately.

Diurnal Cycle

Every human being runs on Nature's clock. A pilot who starts his flying day at eight o'clock in the morning and flies until eight that night would be in reasonably good physical and mental condition, assuming that he slept well the previous night.

But the pilot who starts his flying day at eight o'clock in the evening faces a far different situation. When he is at home, he lives the normal pattern of a family man, and hence finds it difficult to spend the day before a flight sleeping. (I've tried it; it rarely works. Like most men, we're accustomed to sleeping at night).

Well, his flight time begins at eight p.m., two to four hours before his normal sleep cycle. He may spend eight hours at his flight station, and must maintain a peak performance during the flight, and for the landing, which may follow a long and taxing night.

Airport Delay and Fatigue

Air travelers grow accustomed to one variable: airplanes sometimes fail to leave when scheduled.

Perhaps the airplane has arrived late at the airport. Perhaps a member of the ground crew has found some "bug" that must be eliminated. Whatever the reason for the delay, you may be sure that every minute's delay in departure is a minute's further guarantee of your safety. I've never known ground maintenance work to be more efficient than it is as I write this chapter. The men who service the airplane on which you are going to travel are conscientious.

I'm not denying, of course, that such delays can be frustrating, even infuriating. Yet you aren't the only one who is frustrated: the pilot and crew share your sentiments—and with good reason.

Let's assume a typical situation. I'm scheduled to fly an eight-hour non-stop run to Rome, leaving Kennedy Airport, New York City, at 8:00 p.m. I report for duty at 6:00 p.m. to study weather conditions, plan my flight, and so forth. My crew and I go through the usual pre-flight procedures.

Then I find the plane has a mechanical problem, and the flight must be delayed. I settle down to wait, just as the passengers are doing in their lounge. I don't have enough time to drive home for a rest. I've eaten dinner, don't want more coffee, and I don't smoke. Besides, there's a chance that the difficulty will be corrected quickly.

53

But this time, the mechanical delay lasts four hours. By the time I board and sit down at the controls in my cockpit, I've been on duty for six hours.

Now it happens the flight takes longer than anticipated. The winds differ from those forecast, perhaps. Next, traffic makes me deviate from the original flight plan. Instead of an eight-hour flight, it is nine hours—with me at the controls. Thus, when we finally overhead Rome, I have been on duty for fifteen hours. But I'm not quite done!

Weather in Rome has traffic stacked up again: I must hold for thirty minutes ... before making an instrument approach and landing!

Under unavoidable conditions of this sort, rules permit a pilot to work for sixteen hours. (As it happens, I've been on duty many times for something more than sixteen.) I am quite tired by the time I make that instrument landing ...

You, the passenger, undoubtedly feel tired too. On this occasion, we can share the sympathy ...

Liquor and Flying

The subject of alcohol can be divided into two parts, crew drinking and passenger drinking. Let's first talk about the crew.

You have heard that a pilot drinks no alcoholic beverage, strong or mild, for twelve hours before a flight. Most airline companies have their own regulations, which are even more strict than that.

A captain is a mature man whose responsibilities for both human life and expensive property require him to be emotionally adult.

There is a vast difference between the World War I flier who gulped down some liquor, climbed into his open cockpit and then flew his little crate up a few thousand feet—and the captain of a sophisticated jet with a gross weight, when loaded, of almost one third of a million pounds. It is axiomatic that jets and liquor don't mix.

You might say that a mild amount of drinking the day before a flight—one or two social drinks—would not be harmful. But getting drunk and then trying to fly while suffering a hangover the following day would be a stupid, foolhardy and very dangerous risk. There are few, if any, phases of flying more important to a pilot than his reaction time, that is, his ability to respond very quickly—often instantly—to any stimulus or situation. Liquor has a dulling effect, and the man who is enduring a hangover is slowed both mentally and physically. The man who tries to fly an airplane when suffering from a hangover is more than flirting with death. He's deliberately inviting it. Without putting a halo over my own head or the heads of my colleagues, I can only say that all of us are acutely sensitive to this. No, pilot drinking is not a problem these days.

The same is true of other crew members. They're human, so they aren't perfect, but they enjoy living as much as other people, and they have no desire to take a stupid risk that might take their own lives and the lives of others. Airline companies will of course dismiss any flight personnel who disobey the drinking rules.

Passenger drinking is something else again, and I must point an accusing finger at the airlines. Every time I pick up a magazine I read advertisements glorifying the gourmet meals and the superb quality of the wines and other liquor served on flights. In my opinion this emphasis is wrong. I am *not* saying that passengers should be refused liquor on flights. But need we picture the passenger compartment of a jet airliner as a cocktail lounge?

In the days before regulations required the cockpit door to be locked, the drunken passenger was a definite menace to air safety. Even today, the drunken passenger presents us with a safety problem.

Before discussing the matter further, let me emphasize that the overwhelming majority of passengers present no problem. They drink sensibly; it is unusual for a passenger to drink too much on a flight. A company's passenger agent may refuse an intoxicated passenger the right to board an airplane for a flight, even though the individual has a ticket entitling him to a seat. Cabin personnel have the same authority—and use it. Most drunks are weeded out before a flight begins. And cabin personnel are authorized to refuse liquor, in flight, to a passenger who appears to be drinking to excess.

Occasionally, however, one sneaks through. A man—or, less frequently, a woman—appears to be sober when boarding an airplane for a flight. The state of intoxication doesn't become apparent until some time after take-off. Or it may be that the taking of one or two drinks while in the air will push the individual over the edge that separates the sober from the inebriated.

I don't want to raise false alarms. Most drunks are either jolly, or too befuddled to do any harm to themselves or others, although I would hate to depend on someone intoxicated responding rapidly and calmly to evacuation orders in the event of an emergency.

There are "mean" drunks, however, and all pilots and their crews have had to deal with situations created by the belligerent inebriate at one time or another.

Believe it or not, there are no basic rules regarding the handling of the mean drunk. The captain of an airplane has the authority to do whatever he deems necessary for the safety of his passengers, crew and airplane. His position is somewhat similar to that of the steamship captain: he is chief of police, prosecutor, judge and jury. Yet he has no tools to help him enforce order.

Airline hostesses are very adroit in their handling of inebriates, but now and again a drunken passenger will get out of hand, and a hostess will be forced to call on the captain to deal with the situation. This, of course, means he must leave his cockpit, thereby breaking the unrealistic rule forbidding him to leave his flight station. He does this, of course, in exercising his command responsibility.

I recall several problems I've had to handle, all of them incidents that were hazards to safety. The first took place some years ago, back in the days when we didn't lock the cockpit door; in fact, it was a common practice to invite passengers up to the cockpit to watch the airplane being flown.

Anyway, a very large man had been drinking heavily, and apparently had put away a considerable quantity of alcohol before boarding the airplane. He wandered up to the cockpit, and immediately became intensely abusive. He was as mean a drunk as any I've ever seen.

A cockpit is not a place to get into an argument with a drunk. Space is limited, and the damage that could be done if violence broke out is chilling. Well, I tried, as quietly and pleasantly as possible, to pacify him. But the more I said, the wilder he became.

I tried, subtly, to get him out of the cockpit, but he wouldn't budge. I became stern, but that made him even angrier. I didn't want to use force, as he was standing—it might be more accurate to say he was weaving—quite near the controls. But I privately made up my mind that if he as much as reached in the direction of the controls, I would have to use force.

Fortunately, the problem solved itself. The belligerent passenger quietly passed out, just like that. In fact, he collapsed onto the floor of the cockpit. (This created a new, but considerably less acute problem. It would have been difficult to wake him up. In the interest of safety, I left him there on the cockpit floor, snoring, until I had made my landing at the end of the flight.)

The only time I had trouble with a drunken woman passenger created a far more difficult situation. A tiny senorita who spoke no English was obviously very nervous and apprehensive, and I imagine she might have been making her first flight. She had been doing a great deal of drinking before boarding the airplane, although she didn't show it, and one drink during the flight was all she needed to touch her off.

She actually went berserk.

The hostess came to me immediately, and I hurried back to the passenger compartment. I wouldn't have thought that such a small woman could have been so strong; but as physicians and nurses who work with mental patients know, the deranged often display surprising physical strength and stamina.

I don't hesitate to admit that I had my hands full. There was a serviceman among the passengers who volunteered to help, as did another woman passenger who happened to be a registered nurse. Between us we managed to subdue her, but it was some job. Then, because I felt I had no choice, we tied her to her seat until we reached our destination.

The worst problem I've ever had with a drunk took place on a flight over the North Atlantic. A tall, husky male passenger had a drink or two after take-off, and became very disagreeable. He refused to stay in his seat, he tried to provoke other passengers into becoming embroiled in a fist fight with him and he was threatening others who were trying very hard to mind their own business.

One of the hostesses called me back to the passenger cabin, and I spoke to the drunk quietly and pleasantly, asking him to sit down. We talked for some minutes, he finally agreed, and I returned to the cockpit. About fifteen minutes later the hostess reappeared to tell me he was acting up again, and that this time he was creating a lot of trouble.

So I went back to the passenger compartment again, and this time I spoke to the drunk very sternly, ordering him to sit down and stay in his seat. Eventually he obeyed and I directed him to stay there until we landed, which we wouldn't do for another four or five hours.

It was too much to expect that a man in his condition would remain subdued, however. The hostess soon returned to the cockpit for the third time saying that the drunken passenger was completely out of hand. He paid no attention to her, and had become so threatening that some of the passengers were badly frightened.

I found him roaming up and down the aisle, roaring and cursing at the other passengers. My patience was exhausted, and I said so.

He replied, "Captain, if you want to fight with me, you'd better know I used to be a professional boxer."

He was the better part of a head taller than I, and must have outweighed me by thirty pounds or more. But instinct prompted me to say, "Good, so was I. Let's go!" With that, I took off my hat.

Actually, I was bluffing; I haven't been in a fight since I was a small boy in grade school. At any rate, he didn't swing at me. I felt I was getting the upper hand, and after really threatening him, managed to get him back into his seat.

Then I hurried up to the cockpit for the ax that is kept for use in emergencies, and I took it back to the passenger compartment. As it happened, an old friend of mine, a company employee and crew member I've known for years, was making the flight as a passenger. I rearranged the seating, and gave him the place behind the belligerent drunk.

I showed that ax to the drunk, and told him I was ordering the crew member to hit him over the head with it if he so much as moved from his seat again.

Then I said to the crew member-passenger, in a very loud voice, "If this man moves from his seat, hit him over the head with the ax." I was in dead earnest, but meant, of course, that he was to use the blunt end of the ax, and knock the drunk out.

That ended the crisis. The drunk stayed in his seat for the rest of the flight.

I've sometimes wondered, however, what might have happened had he actually swung at me, or had we not been fortunate enough to have a competent employee of the airline traveling as a passenger on that particular flight. I'm aware of no flights in which accidents have been caused by the antics of a drunken passenger. But there can always be a first time, and that incident might result in fatalities.

Other captains can tell stories of trouble they've had with

drunken passengers. But let me comment again that such incidents are rare.

Smoking Rules on Board Airplanes

A rule which does a great deal to insure air safety is the one which forbids passengers to smoke at certain times. But I've found that many people are confused by the rule. Some passengers wonder why they are allowed to smoke after an airplane is airborne, but are forbidden the privilege when the airplane is still safely on the ground.

Let me explain. Except for the relatively few modern telescopic ramps that permit passengers to board an airplane from cabin level, the old passenger loading stairs are still in general use at most airports. That means the passengers walk across the ramp area and then climb a flight of stairs. The ramp area is often soaked with oil and fuel, and a still-lighted cigarette butt, flipped away, could start an exceptionally costly and dangerous fire.

The "No Smoking" sign is always turned on during take-offs and landings because, as the reader knows, these are the most dangerous phases of a flight. If someone should be smoking at the time of an accident, with broken fuel lines or ruptured tanks the risk of fire would be increased, and that risk is already considerable under such circumstances.

There is always an element of risk when passengers, or crew members, for that matter, smoke at *any* time during a flight. It has happened, far too frequently for the peace of mind of captains and their crews, that a passenger inadvertently drops a cigarette behind his seat, setting it on fire.

The most serious fires due to smoking have occurred in the wash rooms. A passenger smokes and then throws the cigarette into the toilet. This is particularly hazardous in the older airplanes using non-flushing chemical toilets. Unless another person enters the room soon thereafter and notices the blaze, a fire can become rather intense.

I do not, however, consider this to be a problem of great seriousness. All jet airlines carry a number of portable H_2O and CO_2 fire extinguishers which are conveniently located in the passenger compartment, so fires caused by cigarettes when an airplane is in flight can be handled without too great a risk. Nevertheless *any* fire in an airplane is dangerous.

Sabotage!

The ugly monster of air travel is sabotage. Murder, including suicide, seems to occur in cycles. In this past year one of the most common forms of murder has been for a madman, armed with one or more guns, to start firing at anyone—relatives, fellow employees, even total strangers. A newspaper report to the effect that someone has killed himself by jumping off a high bridge will, as everyone from psychiatrists to police officials well knows, set off a rash of similar attempts.

It is always open season on commercial airplanes. Some idiot with a grudge against the world or himself plants a bomb in his luggage, takes off and happily awaits mass murder in the sky.

Once in the air, it is almost impossible for a captain to protect his passengers, crew and his company property. When the CAB investigates an accident in which an airplane has suffered mid-air damage other than collision, one of the first things that it seeks is evidence that might indicate a bomb had been planted in the luggage compartment.

Endless meetings of government and airline officials have been held in an attempt to deal with this grave problem. But, incredible though it may seem, the simplest steps to eliminate the hazard have not been removed.

One of the greatest single causes of such tragedies, in my opinion, is the two-bit insurance vending machine. Such machines may be found in virtually every airport of any size and consequence in the United States. There is nothing, literally nothing, to prevent a deranged person who is carrying a time bomb of some kind in his luggage from putting some coins in a slot, making a policy payable to anyone he pleases, and then killing himself (along with many others) in the air.

If an extra large sum is involved, of course, the policy may be opposed. And if specific evidence is found indicating that the airplane was deliberately sabotaged, the insurance companies, may refuse to pay.

But it is inordinately difficult to obtain evidence of this kind. For one thing, when an airplane traveling at a speed of almost six hundred miles per hour explodes many thousands of feet in the air, bits and pieces are scattered over a vast area. Investigators are hunting for the proverbial needle in the haystack. Secondly, in this age of sophisticated technology, bombs can be devised so cleverly that, when they explode, they virtually destroy themselves, leaving few traces.

One of the simplest ways to substantially reduce the possibility of this frightful menace would be to remove all insurance vending machines from all airports. I believe it is the duty of federal, state and local governments to take immediate action outlawing them.

Obviously, laws should be tightened, too, to make it more difficult for the average citizen to gain possession of explosive materials.

The Fear of Air Travel

Some passengers, when they go aloft for the first time, are afraid. Some remain apprehensive, no matter how frequently they travel by air.

I'd like, very briefly, to reassure them. Thousands have felt as they do, and thousands of others will feel the same way. They have no need to be embarrassed or ashamed of what they may believe to be a "weakness." We all fear the unknown.

The men in the cockpit of the airplane in which they are traveling do not share their feeling. We are not operating in the unknown. The best advice I can give the air traveler is this: sit back, buckle your seat belt and relax.

It is possible, of course, for experienced crew members to become "air shy." Just the other day, as this book was being written, I had a brief reunion in Europe, on one of my regular weekly transatlantic flights, with two of the three hostesses, Barbara Pohler and Marion Korn, who although seriously injured survived my Rome accident.

Both required a period of psychiatric care after the crash. Later, one found that she became so nervous in the air that she had to give up her job as hostess and now holds a ground position with TWA. The other went through agonies every time she took off, but managed to sweat it out, and continue flying.

After hearing the travail of these young women, my empathy was renewed for the nervousness of the traveler going aloft for the first time.

Pilots

If I have given the impression that your pilot is a knight in armor riding a jet-powered Pegasus, let me set the record straight. We are neither mighty heroes, nor villains.

Pilots are basically stable men who feel a deep responsibility to the air travelling public. They also feel a sense of loyalty to the companies that employ them, and they are proud of their individual jobs and their profession as a whole.

The responsibility of the pilot for the safety of his passengers, crew, and airplane is also fixed in federal law.

The pilots are often at odds over safety matters with the industry, that is, the government agencies, the manufacturers, and the airlines. These, all too often, join forces against the pilots. The expense factor is delicate. The industry and for that matter the government seeks an "economically balanced" safety level. Not many pilots are willing to compromise the safety goal for economic reasons.

The pilot, finally, has a responsibility to himself, for his personal safety and that of his family.

With all these considerations, you would not expect any pilot to compromise. But safety questions are seldom etched in black and white. As with the "economic balance," there are gray areas of risk.

For example, when the width of the air corridors separating airliners on the North Atlantic run was reduced from one hundred twenty miles to ninety miles—a subject that will be discussed at length in a later chapter—some pilots accepted the ruling.

Then the Air Line Pilots Association and the International Federation of Air Line Pilots made a survey. The results indicated that due to the lack of precise navigational aids an average of one pilot per day strayed from his safe corridor. This does *not* mean that there would be one accident per day from operations outside the narrow corridor; far from it. But it does mean that eventually—in a month, a year, perhaps many years—two airplanes might stray simultaneously and there would be a disaster.

Considering that a pilot on the North Atlantic run crosses the ocean six to eight times per month, on an average, the mathematical odds against his personal involvement in a mid-air collision are slight. Therefore, when the width of the corridor was reduced, some pilots simply took the attitude, "It won't happen to me." They made no protest, took no active part in the fight that eventually resulted in a changed ruling, a reversion to the one hundred and twenty mile corridor.

I am not accusing these pilots of negligence, nor of being indifferent to safety. In my opinion, however, the pilot who says, "Let the other men worry about safety, the statistics look pretty good," is being careless in his basic attitude toward his professional responsibilities.

Pilots earn good salaries, and can enjoy such luxuries as boats, country club memberships and the best schools for their children. A minority in any society prefer not to rock the boat, and take no part in the unending struggle of their colleagues for a higher degree of safety in every aspect of flying. Fortunately, they *are* in the minority.

Most pilots are dedicated to the cause of safety. After all, a captain risks his own life if he accepts flying conditions, equipment, or procedures that provide less than a maximum of safety at all times and under all circumstances. If he's negligent, he can—and should —be grounded. Fortunately, experience is the best of schools. By the time a man has been subjected to the trials, pressures and hazards of flying for many years, the "weak sisters" have dropped out along the way. The man who is promoted from co-pilot to command pilot has demonstrated his proficiency and earned the four stripes he wears on his sleeve. He is a realist in his approach to flying, he is professionally and technically qualified, and is emotionally capable of assuming the burdens that he accepts with his four stripes.

It would be foolish to claim that pilots don't err. But, in the main, their mistakes are honest errors. A pilot would no more become sloppy in operating his airliner than would a surgeon working in a hospital operating room. After all, the pilot is usually the *first* to arrive at the scene of an accident. . . .

V

WEATHER AND SAFETY

Contrary to Mark Twain's often quoted remark that everyone talks about the weather but no one does anything about it, the men who fly and assist in the flight of jet airplanes do a great deal about it. With the aid of modern science, they often in effect "defy" the weather, and airplanes can and do fly today under weather conditions that, some years ago would have grounded everything.

Great strides have been made in creating safer conditions, regardless of the weather. But there are other steps, in my opinion, that are urgently needed in order to make flying as "weather-proof" as human beings are capable of making it. Let's examine the weather from a pilot's viewpoint.

A thunderstorm is one of the most dramatic and violent types of weather encountered in flying, and the inexperienced air traveler frequently considers it the most dangerous. The record indicates otherwise. Relatively few accidents have occurred in thunderstorms. Far more have taken place in "quiet" weather— when there are low ceilings, poor visibility, icing conditions or precipitation, for example.

Airport fogs are common, and can create hazards. Contrary to what most people believe, the most modern airliners do not land completely blind. It is true that blind (instrument) landings have been demonstrated. But in practice, at the last two or three seconds before making contact with the ground, the pilot must actually *see* in order to make the landing. The pilot, when there is fog at an airport, makes an approach by his instruments down to an altitude of approximately two hundred feet. At that point he must have some visual reference to land manually.

Work is being done on new instruments of almost fantastic sensitivity that will enable an airplane to reach a point much closer to the ground before the pilot needs to catch even a glimpse of the runway.

The great problem with fog is that it is difficult to forecast, particularly when airports are located near large bodies of water. In fact, the ability of meteorologists to forecast fog formations has improved very little in the twenty-eight years since I first began to fly.

It remains a constant problem and source of concern to the pilot. For example, let's say an airplane is making a long flight over the North Atlantic from London or Paris to New York. Substantial amounts of fuel have been burned. According to the latest reports the pilot has had from Kennedy Airport in New York, the weather there is clear. Then, as he arrives over his destination, fog suddenly rolls in. He immediately faces two related problems: his fuel supply is limited, so he must consider whether to wait, in the hope that the fog will dissipate, or proceed to another airport.

In Paris, Orly Airport, which is used by jets, is located south of the city, and its problems with fog illustrate the complexities of the jet age. With a high pressure system the prevailing northeast wind, which has a high moisture content, moves across Paris and quickly condenses into fog and smog. Therefore Orly must often close down, particularly during the damp winter months. Le Bourget Field, north of Paris, is less likely to have fog. But this historic airport where Charles Lindbergh landed is not as well equipped as Orly to handle long-range jets.

Any airport located near a large body of water will, under certain weather conditions, fog in quickly. Kennedy, in New York, is located near the water, and so are the fields in Chicago, Cleveland, Boston, San Francisco and Los Angeles. Many airports located in the midwest suffer from what is known as a radiation type of fog, and especially in the autumn, are often forced to suspend operations on foggy nights.

The problems a pilot encounters when landing in a fog are many. He is flying his airplane by instruments, while at the same time trying to identify the runway and other objects on the ground. Sometimes it is very difficult for him to determine how far he has progressed down the runway. His eyes make rapid transitions from the instruments to the outdoors. He must decide promptly if he is in a position to land, or if he must abandon the landing. In this type of landing it is essential that the pilot maintain precise speed control. If he is moving too fast, at the point of commitment, he will find it very difficult to bring the airplane to a halt once he touches down on the runway. But he cannot allow his speed to drop too low because of the possibility of losing control.

Thunderstorms

At the beginning of this chapter I mentioned thunderstorms, and think it would be in order to discuss them more fully. The cell of a thunderstorm is a highly concentrated area of moist air in a boiling action. In the cell are strong, vertical currents of air, some of them moving upward and some downward, in excess of one hundred miles per hour. These rivers of air pick up moisture droplets which, as they move upward, freeze into hailstones; still moving at great speed, they strike with tremendous impact when they come in contact with an airplane that is also moving at a high speed.

In the early, "neolithic age" of flying, it was often impossible to avoid these thunderstorm cells. Every experienced airline pilot flew through many of them in prop planes. I can remember when everyone in the industry believed that once we flew higher than eight thousand to ten thousand feet, we would rise above thunderstorms. But we discovered we were wrong when we flew Constellations and DC-6's at twenty thousand feet, and still found ourselves peering up into the tops of thunderstorms.

Then came the jet age, and pilots breathed a collective sigh of relief. Surely, we thought, jets flying as high as forty thousand feet would move above bad weather. Once again we were wrong, and have since learned that a well-developed thunderstorm can rise as high as seventy thousand to eighty thousand feet or higher.

The jet is far from helpless, however. Airborne radar enables a pilot to identify the cell of a storm, which he can then circumnavigate. If the airplane's radar should fail, however, the exposure to the cell of the thunderstorm is greater.

On February 2nd, 1963, a Northwest Airlines Boeing 720B out of Miami, Florida, flew into a line of thunderstorms, and the aircraft was literally torn apart. It crashed, and all 43 persons on board were killed.

The characteristics of a jet airplane are such that it is dangerous to fly into the cell of a thunderstorm. In fact, pilots will fly hundreds of miles out of their way in order to avoid a thunderstorm. In some instances, when jets have flown into the cells, pilots have temporarily lost control of their ships.

An inherent characteristic of most non-jet airplanes is the tendency to return to level flight when placed in a dive. When the jet dives, however, it has a tendency to dive even more steeply. To solve this problem, jets are equipped with a device known as a "Mach Trim," which electrically and automatically adjusts an airplane's horizontal stabilizers at certain speeds. The device operates like a charm in smooth air, but in rough air the pilot must fight the Mach Trim as well as the weather.

A pilot always had to make certain his airplane was flying fast enough to avoid a stall. Putting the problem in simple aerodynamic terms, enough air had to pass over the wings to maintain sufficient lift to keep the airplane flying, and prevent a stall, with a consequent loss of altitude.

The jet, however, travels at high altitudes, in thin air, at speeds approaching the speed of sound. As the aircraft draws nearer and nearer the speed of sound, shock waves build up, and the jet encounters what is called a "high speed buffet." The back side of a speed curve is what we call a "stall buffet." That is, the air is so thin and the speed of the jet is such that, aerodynamically, the weight of the airplane cannot be supported.

When flying at high altitudes and carrying heavy weights, there is a very narrow margin between the conventional low-speed stall and this high speed buffet. Also, at high altitudes, the airplane's controllability is substantially decreased.

The reader need not be a pilot to realize that if high-speed vertical wind shears are encountered by a heavy airplane at high altitudes, a critical situation can develop very quickly.

Soon after I began to fly jets, I recognized this problem and decided not to plan my flights at the higher altitudes. At altitudes above thirty-seven thousand feet the margin between high-speed buffet and low-speed stall increases substantially. So it is still my operating practice *never* to file a flight plan in excess of thirty-seven thousand feet; I *rarely* file one above thirty-five thousand.

If I am re-cleared to fly at thirty-nine thousand feet due to traffic conditions, let's say, I request either a lower altitude or a rerouting for adequate traffic separation. (The jet airplanes I fly, I might add, are certificated to fly at altitudes up to forty-two thousand feet.)

When a jet is flying through a thunderstorm at a recommended turbulence penetration speed of two hundred eighty knots (approximately twice the turbulence penetration speed of a Constellation) the impact of hailstones, as we have seen, can cause severe damage to the airplane.

Electricity
Electricity is another factor in a thunderstorm. Airplanes

71

flying through clouds or precipitation generate static electricity which sometimes discharges in a bright, dramatic display but seldom causes damage.

Let me illustrate with a personal experience that took place in 1963. I was on a flight from New York to Kansas City, cruising at twenty-six thousand feet, when I learned that a thunderstorm was sitting directly over the airport. I held my airplane northeast of the area until the storm moved off and I was given clearance to land. There was still considerable cloudiness.

I descended rapidly from a mass of cold air—approximately thirty degrees below zero—and moved into an air mass a few thousand feet above the ground—approximately seventy degrees above zero. In other words, within a very short period of time, there was a change of about one hundred degrees.

The combination of the cold airplane and the warm moist highly charged air started an electrical glow on the nose of the airplane. It built up very rapidly to a bright intensity, and then discharged along the left side of the airplane toward the tail. This made a loud, sharp noise similar to the firing of a howitzer.

I was wearing a short-sleeved shirt in the cockpit and could feel on my bare arms the radiated heat from the static discharge. The glow itself was so bright that for a moment it lighted the entire sky.

After I landed, a careful inspection was made of the airplane, and thirty-two burned spots were found. Four of these holes were so deep they actually penetrated the metal skin of the airplane. And the plane was in the shop for some time because the static discharge had magnetized the instrument panels.

Static discharges are common. My experience, however, was unusual. Rarely are they so severe, although under special conditions, static electricity can ignite and cause a partially filled fuel tank to explode.

Lightning, which is more powerful, rarely strikes an airplane, although there have been a few tragic exceptions here also.

Wind

Another weather problem that can sometimes cause concern is wind. Clear air turbulence, that is, wind unaccompanied by clouds or storms, is nothing more than large swirling rivers of air traveling at high speed, mixing with adjacent air.

Wind *can* cause problems on take-offs and landings, and also navigational difficulties, particularly on the North Atlantic run, where flights are long and fuel requirements great. Prevailing winds in the Northern Hemisphere are from west to east: a flight from Europe to the United States may encounter winds ranging from one to two hundred miles an hour.

These winds slow the airplane, which consequently burns a great deal more fuel.

One phase of meteorology that has improved in the jet age is the forecasting of winds aloft; however the pilot is frequently working with forecasts at least eight hours old, so the location of the strong winds can be several hundred miles from the forecast position.

Forecasts

Another phase of meteorology is less improved. One of the pilot's never ending headaches is the accurate forecasting of terminal weather. Let me illustrate.

Just prior to a departure, I'm given a forecast of weather at my destination. Then, somewhere along the way, I hear an actual report, and it indicates that my terminal weather picture is considerably different from the forecast. What kind of weather *will* I encounter when I approach the terminal?

It has been my experience that when there is a widespread area of bad weather (low ceilings, snow, rain, etc.) it is difficult for a pilot to get accurate forecasts. The people who feed us information are reluctant to go out on a limb. I am *not* saying they misinform a pilot. But they will often remain silent for long periods, while a pilot flying anywhere from five to seven miles above the surface of the earth has no idea what weather conditions prevail at his destination.

I am not alone in my feelings, I assure you. In October, 1965, the Master Executive Council of Eastern Air Lines Pilots requested what it called "corrective action on the part of the Weather Bureau" in a resolution called "Meteorological Misinformation." And the Air Line Pilots Association intends to raise the question of what is being called "incorrect weather information" on the agenda of its annual meeting, which is being held a few days after these pages are written.

There is a related problem that is vexing to a pilot, and dangerous. When ceilings are low and visibility is poor, the dispatchers on the ground should be working with a pilot, coordinating all information with him. But at such times, due to the heavy traffic and radio communication congestion, the dispatchers are so busy they often are of little help to the pilot. However, the pilot in his basic qualification is a skilled meteorologist.

It is ironic that when the weather is good and there are no weather problems, a pilot gets a steady stream of forecasts and other help from the ground. But as soon as there is a widespread area of bad weather—low ceilings, poor visibility, rain, snow, icing conditions, whatever—everybody on the ground is too busy and/or the state of the art of meteorology in such that they are of no real help.

Ice

Back in the days when we were flying the DC-3, ice was the pilot's great enemy. A heavy accumulation of ice on the wings was a frightful hazard, but that was only the beginning. Ice formed on the windshield, and a pilot often could not see in front. Therefore he had to open his side window and stick his head out in order to land, just as some people must do to this day when driving an automobile with ice on a windshield. I need hardly add that landing an airplane was trickier and more dangerous than driving an automobile under such conditions.

During World War II, large numbers of combat airplanes being ferried to the European and North African theatres of war were, to my personal knowledge, lost over the Atlantic due to icing of engines and wings. (Experience taught the maneuver of descending over the Gulf Stream if it could be found, to melt the ice.)

But ice has virtually disappeared as a safety hazard in the modern jet, thanks to technological advances. In the pre-jet airplanes, carburetors choked up, causing engines to stall and lose power. Today, although it is true that ice can form on a part of a jet engine, our de-icing system is immediately effective. If a jet loses a little power momentarily, it regains it very quickly. We can also cope with ice on the wings quickly and efficiently. Although ice today presents some problems it is mostly in the mind of the veteran pilot, who, because of past experiences that were nightmares, is still leery of ice. I am, even though I realize the "problem" is mostly psychological.

"Captain, what is the best time of year to fly?"
Pilots are often asked the "best season" to fly.

The two best seasons—and mind you, I'm forced to generalize—are summer and winter. A study of accident records over a period of many years indicates that the fewest take place during the summer months when, generally, weather conditions are good. On the other hand, when flying in northern latitudes in mid-winter, when the weather is very cold, the problems caused by poor visibility and low ceilings occur relatively infrequently.

If there is such a thing as a "worst season," I'd be inclined to name the transitional periods, specifically from autumn to winter and from winter to spring. During these periods there is more snow, more rain, more low ceilings and more poor visibility. There are also airport problems like runways covered with slush or snow that create increased hazards on take-offs and landings.

Diversions to Alternate Airports
You expect to land in New York, but instead, your airplane is

75

diverted to Philadelphia or Boston. You expect to land in Chicago, but instead put down in Milwaukee. And so on.

The neophyte passenger is frequently annoyed, and sometimes alarmed by the diversion of a flight to an alternate airport. The experienced passenger knows that such diversions will occur, and more or less accepts them.

Weather conditions at the intended terminal point of a flight are responsible, in virtually all such instances. Basically, a diversion is a safety operation.

But a new villain is creeping in: clear-weather traffic congestion. Commercial aviation continues to grow at a rapid pace in the jet age, and often airplanes are "stacked up" above an airport, each awaiting its turn to land. Therefore an airplane that is running low on fuel and cannot afford to wait for a long period must proceed to an alternate airport. The passenger is inconvenienced, but he is rarely in danger. In the old days, a pilot might encounter an airport he didn't know, but today most diversions are made to airports with which most pilots are familiar.

Pilots themselves are sometimes unnecessarily responsible for the apprehension felt by passengers when an airplane is diverted. They are remiss in their duties, and fail to inform the passengers why they are diverting. It takes only a few moments to tell the passengers the reasons, and it is a courtesy pilots owe the passengers.

The entire aviation industry—designers and manufacturers, the airlines, government, the pilots—is working on a mammoth program that will enable an airplane to land under virtually all weather conditions.

One of the new systems being developed is the "heads up display." The pilot will control his airplane all the way down, and his instrumentation will be such that, with the aid of an electronic device, the pilot will "see" his approach path all the way to the ground—the actual runway electronically displayed on his windshield.

Under a second, scientifically sophisticated system, the airplane will be controlled by the automatic pilot coupled witȟ an advanced instrument landing system. The pilot will monitor the system until he reaches a point one hundred feet above the runway, at which time he will disconnect the autopilot and, looking out of his window, make the landing himself.

A third system is under study. An automatic pilot, coupled with an instrument landing system, will control the landing all the way to the ground. The pilot will not touch the controls, but will simply monitor the approach and landing.

Most pilots prefer the "heads up" system. We have apprehensions about the second system because of the need to disconnect the automatic feature only one hundred feet from the ground, The margin for error and unexpected problems would be too slim. As for the completely automatic system, we distrust it, too, preferring human judgment and "feel" to that of a machine. Under both of the latter systems, of course, the pilot would be able to assume control of his airplane at any time he so desired. But he would have to take over "cold," without having felt the little peculiarities that can mean so much to smooth approach and landing. This may sound like science fiction to you . . . rest assured, we will insist it is fully tested before becoming operational.

A Study of the Effects of Turbulence

On August 6th, 1966, a Braniff Airways BAC 111 crashed near Falls City, Nebraska, killing forty-two persons. And that accident has reopened a sore subject.

In the early 1960's turbulence, either in clear weather or in storms, was responsible for six airliner accidents, but changes in flight procedures seemed to have the problem solved. Now, however, Civil Aeronatics Board investigators have tentatively ruled out sabotage, mid-air collision or an encounter with a stray object as possible causes of the Falls City crash. Turbulence—specifically the matter of how well a jet can withstand the violence of turbulent air—may be responsible.

Let's look at this accident in some detail. A piece of the right wing was found about one-half mile from the greater part of the wreckage ... to the side. Also, a part of the tail was found three-quarters of a mile away ... to the rear.

CAB investigators know that the pieces broke off in the air, well before the moment the airplane struck the ground.

Some observers speculated on "metal fatigue" caused by vibrations and the other strains of ordinary flight. A microscopic examination of the torn edges indicated "overstress," that is, sudden forces too great for the metal to withstand, was the cause.

Theory and eyewitness reports indicated the tearing of the wing caused the fuel inside to form a "mist" around the aircraft, and it caught fire before the crash.

In somewhat similar crashes in the past, like that of a Northwest Orient airliner over the Florida Everglades in 1963, the CAB believed that the way the ship was being handled was partly responsible—that the airplane was caught in a violent updraft, and, as the pilot adjusted his controls in order to cope with the situation, a violent downdraft struck the airplane ending all control and tearing it apart.

But in the Nebraska crash there are indications that *the airplane was ripped apart while in level flight rather than while in a dive.*

A few other facts are known. The Braniff ship was making her way through a squall line, avoiding the cells, of course. She had slowed her speed to approximately three hundred miles per hour. And at one point in her flight she had been about forty miles off planned course, her pilot deviating deliberately to avoid the worst weather.

There are substantial design differences between a jet and a propeller airplane. A jet wing is swept back and has more flexibility. This gives it different aerodynamic responses. In general, everyone in the industry has been happier with the jets, because they are more rugged.

For example, a PAA Boeing 707 went into a dive of more than

five miles in 1959, and pulled out so sharply that the wings had to withstand forces five times or more the force of gravity! The wings warped, but the pilot managed to make a safe landing. And on two other occasions that I know of (there may have been others as well) jets have managed to achieve successful landings after *losing* large sections of their wings.

But the Nebraska accident resurrects questions that had been buried for several years. Jets are admittedly new airplane types. Not even the men who design them know *all* the answers yet. Is it possible that their special characteristics can create unforseen problems in clashes with the elements? Would turbulence like that in the storm over Nebraska have destroyed any airplane, propeller or jet, or is the jet in more danger?

The manufacturers cannot answer this with complete authority, any more than the designer. Man has not conquered the weather, and he cannot even predict the effect of various conditions on a jet. At least, no individual or group of analysts and predictors with all the answers is known to pilots.

VI

HAZARDS IN THE AIR, OBVIOUS AND HIDDEN

Safety Versus Glamour

Has the race of the airlines for the passenger's dollar been harmful to safety? Would money being spent in glamour advertising to attract the consumer be better spent making air travel safer?

Statistics can be juggled to answer these questions from any point of view. "Figures don't lie," as the saying goes, "but liars figure." My own answer is, I wish the airlines concerned themselves a little less with the glamour of air travel, and more with safety.

If you ride first class, you'll sit in a fairly comfortable seat, and will be served a multi-course meal, cooked on board; you'll also drink "on the house" (although, of course, you'll actually have paid for your food and liquor when you bought your ticket). If you travel tourist or economy class, depending on the semantics of the individual airline, your seating arrangements will be somewhat less comfortable, but nevertheless adequate. Your meal will either be cold or pre-cooked and reheated; in either event, it will be less lavish than that served in first class. In some cases, you'll buy your drinks.

Regardless of which class you travel, you'll be given a reasonable baggage allowance. Perhaps you'll listen to music, watch a movie, either on a full screen, with personal earphones, or on a small set just for you. You'll arrive at your destination, where your luggage will either be handled efficiently and quickly, or else you'll have to wait for it, depending on the system being utilized by the individual airline—all of whom are working toward greater dispatch in baggage handling.

What, then, is all the fuss about? Madison Avenue advertising experts know that two things they can never oversell are sex and good food. Therefore virtually every airline boasts, in its advertising, of its superb cuisine, its excellent service, and the beauty, charm—and even the eye-catching uniforms—of its hostesses. Millions of dollars are spent annually stressing these subjects.

Human nature can't be changed, I suppose; I shouldn't complain. Nevertheless, I comment. To an extent, the fault is not that of the airlines, but basically the traveling public is to blame. Some passengers become impatient when they think the "No Smoking" sign has been on for too long, or because a hostess is a little tardy bringing them their whiskey and soda. What *should* make them impatient is whether adequate steps have been taken to insure their safety.

Far more important than the excellence of their drinks, the broiling of their steaks or the design of their hostesses' costumes should be this checklist. Passengers should know—and demand to be told—that there is an emergency exit located two seats forward. What's more, they should know precisely how to use that exit. If there is no exit within fifteen or twenty seats, they should ask what escape arrangements *are* adequate for their safety, and they shouldn't just make casual inquiries when chatting with a hostess.

The inquiries should also be directed, in writing, to the airline . . . and to the airplane manufacturer. Try the company president. Or the Administrator of the FAA . . . he should be as responsible for your safety as is the Public Health Service or the Food and Drug Administration.

The airlines maintain continuous programs of checking cabin

personnel, hostesses and pursers. Unfortunately, some checking supervisors worry more about the shade of hostess' lipstick and the length of her hair than whether she is thoroughly familiar with the emergency equipment on board the airplane. They will fuss over her ability to prepare a steak properly, but too often fail to find out whether she has reviewed all emergency procedures recently. They will test her ability to serve a chilled drink far more often than they will test her ability to activate those emergency chutes.

In spite of the lack of concentration by supervisors on what I consider the essentials, I am proud of the hostesses and pursers who fly with me. They take professional pride in their work. Certainly the lack of stress on safety is not their fault. If passengers demand to be told that there are life jackets under the seats, and insist they be shown how to use them, the airlines will respond accordingly.

It stands to reason that people who are informed are less likely to become panicky in case of emergncy: If the public is better educated, lives can be saved.

Mid-Air Collisions

Collisions in the air are a nightmare to pilots, as well as to everyone else in aviation. It is a problem that grows more serious as traffic increases. The private airplane, once a symbol of great wealth, is now common, and proliferating at a rapid rate. Hence the danger of collisions between jets and light airplanes is a growing menace, particularly during departure and approach, when the jets are operating at the same altitudes as the light airplane.

Generally speaking, all traffic close to airports is under radio control and radar surveillance However, a vast amount of traffic is flying under visual flight rules, and many airplanes are piloted by people whose experience is limited.

The high speeds of jets substantially increase the risks of collisions. The closing rate, that is, the rate at which two airplanes approach each other, is rapid, and thus the time in which one or both can take evasive action is reduced.

The separation of most high level traffic in the United States is under ground control, and is strictly supervised. But some military airplanes engaging in maneuvers are not controlled, and sometimes fly hazardously near commercial airliners. The traffic dangers are further increased by the large private airplane, usually corporate-owned. These include jets.

The statistics on collisions and near-collisions are shocking. There are approximately five hundred traffic control incidents and near-misses in the United States annually that reach the record books. I believe the actual number is higher, since some pilots are afraid of criticism and fail to report their near misses.

A list of fatal mid-air collisions that have occurred to airliners in the last two decades tells its own grim story:

TWA airliner and a light airplane over Kansas City.

PAA airliner and a private airplane over Long Island Sound.

TWA airliner and a private airplane over Cincinnati.

UAL and TWA planes over Grand Canyon.

UAL and TWA planes over Brooklyn, N.Y.

PAA and EAL planes south of Kennedy Airport, New York.

TWA and EAL planes over Carmel, Conn.

Capital Airlines plane and National Guard airplane over Maryland.

UAL plane and a military aircraft over Nevada.

AA and UAL planes over Michigan.

EAL plane and a military aircraft over New Jersey.

EAL plane and a military aircraft over Washington, D.C.

EAL plane and a supplemental airline plane near Washington, D.C.

If there are five hundred reported incidents and near-misses per year now, and if traffic continues to grow, as it inevitably must, the number of mid-air collisions is certain to grow too, unless decisive action is forthcoming. And when two airplanes collide in the air, there are seldom any survivors.

Hazards in the Air, Obvious and Hidden

The solutions to the mid-air collision problem are plain.

All aircraft, military, civilian and commercial must comply with air traffic rules and, most important, every airplane, large and small, must be equipped with electronic collision warning devices; these are now developed, and further delay is inexcusable.

Jet Approaches and Landings

Like a take-off, an approach and landing require the utmost skill. Jets are even less "forgiving." The pilot must be precise: his speed, altitude and flight control simply cannot be sloppy.

In order to understand it, let's first examine what happens in the landing of a small, light, single-engine airplane. Under ideal conditions the pilot will plan his approach so his airplane will touch down fairly near the beginning of the runway. First he maneuvers into position for the landing. He aligns himself with the runway. Then, at the right height and at the moment he knows from experience to be right, he slowly starts moving his elevator control stick back in one gentle movement—at the same speed from beginning to end, neither varying it nor jerking. When he has pulled the stick as far as it will go, the airplane—at that very instant—touches down in a perfect three-point landing. This is a technique that every pilot learns in his basic training.

A clear weather approach landing in a jet should be *somewhat* the same. Once the landing approach is begun, there is a gradual, steady reduction of speed until the touchdown, at which point the airplane should be close to its stall speed.

Established procedures permit only two departures from the ideal: first, a five-knot variation is permitted when winds in excess of twenty knots per hour are blowing on the earth's surface; and second, an allowance is made for half of the wind gust factor.

In actual practice, however, the established procedures are too rigid. There are many factors that affect the approach and landing of an airplane, *particularly* the heavy, very fast jet. The

85

procedures fail to take into consideration rain, snow, sleet and fog. Visibility may be reduced by haze, smoke and dust. There are wind shears, crosswinds, tailwinds and temperature variables. Humidity is a factor, as are the actual terrain and possible obstructions, either on the approach or on the ground. Gusts are often tricky and unreliable, and consequently are not the same as those reported to the pilot prior to his landing.

Nevertheless, the pilot is required to "fly by the numbers," as it is called. Only the two variables are recognized, when in reality there are many others.

Let's consider a situation in which an instrument approach to a landing is required because of bad weather. The pilot must adhere to his appropriate reference speed. *That speed, under some of the adverse conditions, is very close to the margin of safety, too close for my peace of mind.*

Among the unpredictables, consider wind shear, for example. The pilot begins his approach at, perhaps, two thousand to three thousand feet and makes a steady, continuous descent. Wind velocity and direction may change abruptly. The "numbers game" will not always work. If the pilot is flying very close to the minimum safe speed, and encounters sudden, unexpected wind shear close to the ground, he finds himself and his aircraft in a critical position. *This has happened many times, both in my own experience and in that of other pilots with whom I have discussed the problem.*

Following several accidents—three, to my own personal knowledge—some of the "numbers" have been changed. But they are still insufficiently elastic.

Let's continue with our illustration of the jet landing under adverse runway and weather conditions. At the moment the pilot makes contact with the ground he becomes exceptionally busy, and his professional abilities are taxed to their limit.

Keep in mind that most runways are really inadequate for jet operations. They are too short, or too narrow, or both. Now, due to the weather, the runway on which the pilot lands is also wet

86

and slippery. His giant aircraft (gross landing weight of more than two hundred thousand pounds) is moving at a speed of up to one hundred fifty miles per hour. This mass must be halted on a slick surface, and stay on the runway. (It is common, I might add, to find ditches and obstructions at the sides and ends of the runway.)

Continuing the possibilities, the brake adjustment may be less than perfect. Also, when thrusts are reversed, there is always the risk that one engine may not respond. This can cause an asymmetrical thrust, which can veer the airplane. On the fan jet airplanes in particular, it is common for the reverse power application to respond unevenly, due to the thrust cable rigging.

There is also the problem of the "hydroplaning effect." When water gets under the front portion of the wheels, it creates conditions similar to those found in water-skiing. Even less than one-half-inch of water fully covering the runway can reduce friction to zero at any speed for any airplane weight due to the hydroplaning effect, and this renders the wheel brakes ineffective!

The pilot should be allowed to deviate from procedures when, in his professional opinion, conditions demand it.

There are still other jet landing problems. At some airports there are poor instrument landing facilities. At others the lighting facilities just pass the minimum requirements, and by my standards are feeble. A pilot's nightmare is a black runway. When landing on one at night, in adverse weather, when lighting is poor, I always feel that I am putting my airplane into a big, black hole.

Landing—Just in Time

I was flying into England's London Airport, on a routine flight. The field had fogged in during the night, and now, in the early morning, the airplanes coming in were required to hold above the airport until the fog lifted enough for landing purposes.

My place in the "holding stack" was twenty-eight thousand feet, and about five minutes after I moved into my slot, a Russian TU-112 arrived. (Like the Boeing 707 and the Douglas DC8, this is a large jet capable of making intercontinental passenger flights.) It was assigned a place one thousand feet above me.

Almost immediately after he moved into place, airplanes began to land, one by one, peeling off from the bottom of the stack in response to the ground traffic controller. Visibility had improved to about one mile, perhaps one and one-half miles, which was enough for a landing.

The captain of the Russian airplane radioed in, told the controller he lacked sufficient fuel to await his turn, and said he had to come in immediately. In effect, he was declaring an emergency.

The controller gave him clearance to come in first, from the other side of London. That meant he could descend without danger of collision with the airplanes that were flying in the holding stack. He descended and was then given clearance number one to approach London Airport.

Unfortunately, he missed his approach; that is, when he descended to a minimum altitude, either he was unable to see the field, or he was not correctly aligned with the runway. He therefore had to pull up and make a "go-around."

When he called the tower to say he was pulling up, it was obvious to everyone in the holding stack listening to the conversation that there was concern in his voice. To put it bluntly, he sounded shaky.

The controller sensed his worry, and asked him how much fuel he had left. Five minutes worth was the nervous answer.

This meant he scarcely had time to circle the field for an instrument approach. If he missed it a second time, he was certain to crash.

The tension in the holding stack became as thick as the fog.

The London controller was superb, and immediately took action. He had the Russian on his radar scope, and literally guided him to a landing, vectoring him into position and lining him up by giving him headings to the runway. The Russian landed safely, and everyone in the holding stack breathed more easily.

The entire operation had taken three minutes at most . . . which was all it *could* take. Normally, he would have made an approach by the instrument landing system, which would have taken six or eight minutes, and there was always the danger that he would have missed again.

All of us in the holding stack had flown considerable distances, from such cities as New York and Chicago. The incident caused a thirty-minute delay, in all, before other airplanes began to land. Our own fuel supplies were limited but we certainly operated on a far greater margin of safety than did the Russian pilot!

Russia may or may not be ahead of the United States in the race to outer space. But when it comes to jet travel, I'll fly in an American airplane, thanks, rather than in one which would present no fuel margin for safety.

Fire Warning Systems

The reader is already aware of the hazard of fire. A fire can break out—on take-off, in flight, or during the approach and landing—without the knowledge, in some cases, of the pilot and his crew. Therefore, it is of prime importance that jet airplanes be equipped with the most foolproof fire warning system that man is capable of devising.

Despite all the years of experience, we now find that jet systems are not so designed.

In my Rome accident, the generator was dislodged by the collision with the steamroller, and there was no electric power for the fire warning system emergency switch.

The Commission urged in its section devoted to technical recommendations: "Devise a way to power the fire alarm system in parallel with every other source of electrical power aboard."

Perhaps we should return to the proven "hot-line" system (direct from the battery) that would function in the event of a single generator system's failure, or the simultaneous failure of all systems. This problem was, in fact, resolved in the days of the propeller airplane: warning systems *were* electrically wired to work when one or more engines lost their generators.

A paragraph was recently added to the emergency section of my own flight handbook: "Experience has shown that serious damage to the aircraft can be incurred on the ground with very little indication to the cockpit crew. Be suspicious of any indication, and if there is any question as to airplane damage, accomplish the following: (a) stop the aircraft; (b) start levers off; (c) pull all fire pulls; (d) discharge the fire extinguishers to each engine; (e) immediately determine the need for passenger evacuation.

If we are capable of designing, building, and flying powerful and sophisticated machines like the jet airplane, we can take into account every fire that has ever caused destruction of life on these airplanes.

Fire is the big killer. We must reduce it to an absolute minimum.

VII

NOISE ABATEMENT PROGRAMS—AND SAFETY

When Orville and Wilbur Wright cranked up their first home-made airplane engine, their neighbors probably complained of the noise the machine made. The number of airplanes in operation has been increasing ever since, and so have the complaints.

In the years prior to World War II, civic groups or local politicians sometimes asked airports to deviate temporarily from normal take-off and landing patterns, usually when large open-air gatherings were going to be held. After the war, with the advent of the four-engine aircraft, the noise became worse, and the public began to clamor for relief. Public drives were organized, press agents were hired, and it was not uncommon to get the threat that mothers would be rolling baby carriages onto airport runways.

At one point the furor became so great that the Port of New York Authority closed the Newark, New Jersey airport for a time. That, however, was just the beginning. Aircraft noise was termed a major nuisance; beyond a certain PNDB, or perceived noise decibel count, the sound of airplanes was deemed injurious to health and harmful to property; a new science was born.

Lawsuits became commonplace, and more important politicians jumped into the arena on both sides, both to defend and attack the airplane. Inevitably, a profession was created, the noise abaters.

Then came the jet. Anyone within a half-mile or so of the turbojet, with its king-sized blowtorch sound and its banshee compressor wail, knows he isn't listening to a lullably. The complaints rose to a roar.

And truly, people living in the vicinity of airports used by jets were in a bedlam. Sleep was interrupted, as were church services, school classes and social gatherings.

We pilots, like everyone else in the aviation industry, were on the defensive. I must admit that we secretly agreed with John Casey, the manager of the old Midway Airport in Chicago, who told control tower operators, ticket agents, pilots, dispatchers and the police to refer all complaints to him. "I'm sorry, friend," he would then say when the citizens telephoned him, "but you bought yourself a house close to the railroad track."

The Federal Aviation Agency and airport authorities entered the picture, and established noise abatement regulations, some of them effective and some considerably less so. The problem continues to grow, and is mushrooming to such an extent that I believe air safety has been jeopardized.

The end is not in sight. The noise made by the present-day jet will sound like a baby's whisper when the SST—the supersonic jet—booms its way through the sound barrier.

The problem is double-edged. Modern airplanes make noise, and those of tomorrow will be still noiser. *But programs of noise abatement should not be allowed to increase any risk factor of the jet*. On the other hand, every citizen is entitled to quiet, to be spared noise that may be harmful to him or might damage his property.

The dilemma is typical of our present age. There is a growing demand for rapid, inexpensive travel, the type that can be provided only by a fast jet carrying many passengers. The development of that travel, however, is difficult.

It is not my place to determine how the public should pay for that progress. My concern remains the problem of air safety. And it is for that reason that I analyze these noise abatement programs.

To understand the whole tricky question, let's follow a fully-loaded, Europe-bound jet taking off from Kennedy Airport, using Runway 31-left. As the speed builds up to approximately one hundred and eighty miles per hour, the pilot pulls back on the control wheel. The nose wheel slowly leaves the ground. After rolling another few hundred feet, the dragon of the air becomes airborne at a speed of approximately two hundred miles per hour.

The captain commands the co-pilot to retract the landing gear as the airplane nears the end of the runway. When the aircraft reaches an altitude of only three hundred feet the mandatory noise abatement procedure begins. The captain is required, by law, to make a turn of twenty degrees to the left. During this maneuver he is flying at the marginal speed required to keep the ship in the air. Certainly he does not have enough altitude to recover from a possible stall.

The captain is focusing his attention on his air speed indicators, since the speed factor is so critical. He must also watch the horizon indicator, the compass and the directional indicator.

Then he is required, by law, to reduce the power of his engines in order to lessen the noise!

There are test stations at Kennedy Airport that record the noise made by his jet engines, in decibels; if he does not reduce his power at this moment, he can expect a prompt form demanding an explanation . . . At the same time, of course, the law instructs him to disregard requirements that jeopardize safety. Well, the FAA is quite in the clear—but they are not flying the airplane. Many pilots, in this dilemma over a test station, reduce their power to lower the reading on the testing machine—then increase their power immediately after passing the spot. A program reduced to a farce!

Putting aside all questions of noise, and speaking exclusively as the pilot responsible for the passengers, crew, and airplane, I consider it shocking that the huge, heavily loaded jet, barely able to remain in the air because of its low speed and low altitudes, should be required by government regulation to flirt with the laws of aerodynamics.

A substantial reduction of the pilot's safety margin for error is a devilish procedure.

He should be benefiting from the speed and power which his jet is capable of achieving, to make the take-off safer, and I would call a safe speed for controllability in a heavily loaded jet two hundred fifty miles an hour. Additionally, those on the ground would benefit, more than any other way, from allowing the pilots to take advantage of the excellent climb capabilities of the jet. Altitude lessens noise on the ground more than anything else.

Back to the single most dangerous moment of the flight. If an instrument fails, if an engine fails, if turbulent air is encountered, if any one of the systems fails—in fact, if anything happens that might even momentarily divert the pilot's attention from actual flying (not to mention his legal obligation to watch for other planes in order to avoid a mid-air collision)—the flight is at the edge of disaster.

Let me add that the speed at which he is climbing is *less* than the required minimum in case *two* engines fail. I, and every pilot I know, feel we are jeopardizing human life if we follow these exacting procedures. And I'm afraid that the very forces that are coercing us into compromising safety will be very unforgiving when disaster strikes.

It won't be the first time. On March 1st, 1962, an American Airlines jet took off from Kennedy Airport, followed a noise abatement procedure and crashed into Jamaica Bay, killing everyone on board. The subsequent investigation indicated there had been a mechanical failure in the rudder system.

It is my belief that had the airplane taken off and made a normal, safe climb-out, gaining air speed and altitude in a normal manner, there would have been no crash. I feel certain the pilot would have been able to control his airplane and keep it in the air despite the mechanical failure. But with power reduced, it was hanging on the verge of uncontrollability.

A pilot's proficiency is demonstrated at least three times each year. Do you realize that if a pilot had made a take-off five years ago, following the gyrations, power-cuts, etc. required by today's noise abatement procedures, he would have failed his flight check and possibly have lost his license for engaging in reckless flying at low altitude.

Let me cite a personal experience. In December, 1965, I was scheduled to make a flight from New York to Madrid. I took off in a snowstorm, into a northeast wind. Procedure required a turn to the right, soon after take-off.

The snow was wet and showed a tendency to stick to the airplane. I realized there was a possibility the snow might freeze on my wing and, before I could get rid of it, reduce the aerodynamic lifting potential. So I did not reduce my power at the appropriate time for noise abatement purposes. Instead I maintained full take-off power until I had gained sufficient altitude and air speed to fly safely.

On my return to New York, I was not surprised to find a letter in my mailbox, informing me I had exceeded the noise level permitted.

Noise abatement is a puzzle that no one has been able to solve. Everyone is in favor of it, yet no one quite knows what to do about it. In fact, on March 26th, 1962, when Mr. Halaby was Administrator of the Federal Aviation Agency, he declared in a letter to Captain A.D. Heath of TWA, "I do wish to make the position of the Federal Aviation Agency clear with respect to noise abatement procedure. Safety is a fundamental responsibility, and no procedure for noise abatement, or for any other purpose which creates an unacceptable level of safety, will be approved by us. Noise is a secondary consideration."

The airlines are caught in the same trap as the men who fly their airplanes. With one hand they try to accept the dictates of the noise abatement program, but, at the same time, they are busy with the other trying to shore up the safety of flying operations.

On March 27, 1962, a bulletin from Robert Mueller, Assistant Vice President of Operations for TWA, sent to me and my fellow pilots entitled, "Noise Abatement," said: "Much has been published about noise abatement in the past two or three years. This bulletin is not intended to review the noise problem, but to bring into focus situations caused by the noise problem. *The most important point to be stressed is the fact that published procedure should be followed.*" (The italics are mine, not Mr. Mueller's.)

But later, in the same communication, he turned over the coin, and wrote: "Even though a noise abatement take-off has been pre-planned, it may be necessary to abandon the procedure due to turbulence, heavy precipitation, or air traffic control requirements after the take-off has been started. Do not hesitate to abandon the procedure if, in your opinion, conditions warrant this decision."

Forgive the captain of a jet airliner, please, if he becomes more than slightly concerned. And so it is that our Air Line Pilots Association has taken a strong stand on the subject. The board of directors recommended: "*The Association maintains the position that aircraft noise should be reduced by engineering and design, and not by marginally safe techniques.*" (The italics are mine.)

At this same meeting the following resolution was passed: "Therefore, be it resolved that the Air Line Pilots Association refuses to endorse or accept noise abatement procedures which require: (1) clearances or communications designed to change headings at low altitudes for noise abatement purposes; (2) turns below six hundred feet for noise abatement purposes; (3) reduction of power purely, or to a greater extent, than is done on a normal take-off; (4) climbs at speeds less than maneuverable speed for the existing flap configuration; (5) procedures when weather is below a one thousand foot ceiling and three miles of visibility; (6) preferential runway for noise abatement purposes when (a) the runways are wet, (b) crosswind of greater than ten miles velocity or wind angle which exceeds eighty degrees."

A fine safety resolution, but impossible to implement. Beyond the very limited degree consonant with his judgment on every flight, a pilot cannot fly safely and reduce the noise made by an aircraft that *is* noisy. The ability of the airline to cooperate in noise abatement programs is also limited, and so is that of the Federal Aviation Agency.

If people object to a jet's noise—and I honestly can't blame anyone living near an airport for objecting—let them demand that the designers and their engineers find ways to build a quieter jet engine. Such efforts are being made, of course. Vast sums of money are being spent in the research and development departments of every jet airplane manufacturing company to create new engines that will reduce the decibel count of jet engines to a level that the private citizen will find tolerable.

The problem of aircraft noise bothering people indoors at least has been solved by some of the modern airport hotels.

The general public must understand, however, that the problem is complex, and cannot be solved overnight. It is even more complicated in the design of the forthcoming SST, or supersonic transport, which will crash through the sound barrier.

I shall merely indicate the severity of the problem by quoting from U.S. Senate Document No. 90 (May 19th, 1966), the Staff Report prepared for the use of the Aeronautical and Space Sciences: "With the advent of the supersonic transport many more people, of the order of *tens of millions*, will be exposed to a sound that is as noisy or as objectionable as that now experienced under the flight path of a jet aircraft about $1\frac{1}{2}$ miles from an airport."

Everyone in the aviation industry is working to the best of his ability towards noise abatement. I must go on record, however, as saying that in my job, safety is more important than noise abatement.

97

VIII

THE NORTH ATLANTIC STORY

Modern Traffic Build-Up

The middle-aged can recall with ease the days when the automobile was a luxury rather than a necessity, when driving a car was joy rather than a major hazard, and when traffic was either light or nonexistent. Well, the airplane's leap from the wild blue yonder to the age of super-congestion has been even more rapid. The technology of commercial aviation is so rapid that airports have been left far behind, and many have become obsolete. Airlanes are choked, increasing the risk of mid-air collisions. And the worst is yet to come. According to an estimate made by *The New York Times* on August 24, 1966, airport traffic will be *double* its present volume by 1970. Airplane manufacturers are currently working on aircraft that will carry as many as four hundred ninety passengers, and major airlines have already placed orders for such ships.

According to an FAA estimate, delays in take-offs and landings cost the airlines, at an estimated $3.17 in crew cost, fuel and maintenance for each minute of delay, $63,500,000 for 1965!

June 7th 1963 has often been called "Black Friday" by the airway traffic controllers. On that day, the FAA traffic center at Islip, Long Island, which controls air traffic in New York, New Jersey, parts of Connecticut, and portions of Pennsylvania, handled almost 3,700 instrument operations, 400 above its previous top volume. (The normal daily total in that year, I might add, was 2,000 instrument operations. During the hours of greatest congestion on Black Friday, between 4:00 and 10:00 p.m., the average delay in take-off from Kennedy Airport was one hour and twenty minutes!)

Passengers are irritated, and the airlines are searching for ways and means to handle the growing volume of traffic. Meanwhile, in spite of the congestion, they are continuing to keep their stockholders happy. On international and domestic routes, the scheduled American airlines flew 94,743 passengers in 1965. This represented an increase of 15.9% over 1964, and of 127.2% over a period of ten years.

That picture appears to be bright. But there are dark clouds on the horizon. Future profits depend on the continuing growth of the industry, and that growth may be hampered, beyond repair, by the problems of congestion.

Safety Squeeze Over the North Atlantic

The most graphic way to explain the problems of congestion, and the consequent increase in safety hazards, I believe, is to examine the subject of air traffic over the North Atlantic. At first glance it may seem inconceivable that there could be "traffic" problems over an area so vast, but for basic operational reasons, the problems are grave.

Most Europe-bound flights depart during "rush hour" periods, between 4:00 p.m. and 10:00 p.m., as previously noted. This means that the heaviest outbound traffic from the United States is compressed into one quarter of the twenty-four hour day.

Intercontinental jets fly best at certain altitudes, encountering less weather and burning less fuel. In general, they function at their maximum efficiency between thirty-one thousand and thirty-nine thousand feet. Then, within these margins, they take the route, on each flight, in which weather forecasts have indicated the most favorable wind conditions. Therefore the range is narrowed still more.

100

Now, let's consider several other factors. Over-ocean navigational track-keeping has improved somewhat, in my more than twenty years of transatlantic flying, but it is still less than pinpoint precise. In fact, some airplanes are flying the North Atlantic with what are basically the same equipment and methods that were used during World War II. Today's airliners stray substantially from their planned tracks. It is routine for an airplane to stray thirty miles off course, and common for it to stray fifty miles off course. These figures are based on a survey made by the transatlantic pilots, about which I'll have more to say shortly. This same survey, I might add, indicated that occasionally flights with defective navigational equipment strayed one hundred miles off course.

Consider the record of our space program, in which astronauts have splashed down more accurately after circling the earth many times than we track over the North Atlantic. But there are no requirements for the new devices in either civilian or military airplanes flying the North Atlantic.

Let me clarify this point. The devices and systems presently in use on airliners are totally safe for the purpose of navigating from point A to point B; however, they are *not* sufficiently accurate and dependable for the purpose of keeping airliners in narrow traffic corridors across the North Atlantic.

Operation Accordion

Jets fly across the Atlantic at altitudes of 31,000, 33,000, 35,-000, and 37,000 feet. They are stacked carefully with these 2,000-foot cushions separating them vertically. This is essential. The altimeter is something of a precision instrument in the lower atmosphere; but higher, in thin air and greater air speeds, the altimeter error is magnified.

The airplanes are also separated in time. A plane that leaves New York at 6:00 p.m. might fly at the same altitude as one that leaves New York at 6:30 p.m., but as the two maintain the same speed accurately, the chance they will collide is remote.

The third separation is a lateral corridor arrangement. Each corridor is one hundred twenty miles wide, and every airplane flying the Atlantic has a track with a safe corridor. No other plane flying in the same direction or opposite will come within one hundred twenty miles of it—in theory.

However, it is common for an airplane to stray as much as fifty miles from its track . . .

Assume, for a moment, that a jet flying from the United States or Canada to Europe strays fifty miles to the south. Meanwhile an airplane flying from England to the United States, in the adjoining corridor, strays fifty miles to the north. Those two airplanes will be flying fairly close to each other, close to the margin of safety—but not too close, in the opinion of the International Association of Air Transport, a group comprised of the management of airline companies!

More and more airplanes are flying across the Atlantic every year. Airline schedules are increasing. And the airline companies, as a consequence, made appeals to the four governments that control traffic over the North Atlantic (the United States, Great Britain, Portugal and Canada) to reduce the width of the lateral corridors. Obviously, if the corridors were narrower, more airplanes could be flown. They argued that the corridors could safely be reduced from one hundred twenty to ninety nautical miles.

The pilots had visions of mid-air collisions and objected strenuously. At a meeting of the International Civil Aviation Organization, held in Montreal in the spring of 1965, representatives of the American Air Line Pilots Association and of the International Federation of Airline Pilots Associations strongly opposed a recommendation of the International Civil Aviation Organization for such a reduction.

The United States Government, represented by the FAA, jumped to the carriers' call and approved a twenty-five percent reduction of the lateral corridor, from one hundred twenty miles to ninety miles, commencing on February 7th, 1966.

Less than a week later the Air Line Pilots Association formally petitioned the FAA to hold public hearings on the matter in the interests of safety. In the meantime, as a precautionary measure, the Association urged its pilots to request a separation of one hundred twenty miles on their flights (which the FAA had said would continue to be available below an altitude of twenty-nine thousand feet, when traffic permitted).

Let me interject here that no pilot enjoys flying an intercontinental jet below twenty-nine thousand feet. A jet burns more fuel at lower altitudes than it does flying in the 31,000-37,000 foot range, but a lower altitude was safer than a narrow corridor.

On March 3rd, 1966, the Air Line Pilots Association made a second appeal to the FAA. Its president, Charles H. Ruby, said that the Association "is particularly alarmed that data already supplied to the FAA has failed to persuade the Agency that an urgent problem exists even though pilot technical experts have, on the basis of the same data, concluded that prompt remedial action is necessary if the highest degree of safety is to be maintained without interruption."

Capt. Ruby further questioned the reliability of studies called *Project Accordion*, which supposedly proved that lateral separation could be safely reduced. In his letter to the FAA, he said, "Far from conclusively proving that lateral separation can be safely reduced, *Project Accordion* provides an inadequate and unreliable foundation for action. Much evidence suggests that *Project Accordion* relies on distorted, biased data which grossly underestimates the frequency and magnitude of deviation from track."

On March 15th, 1966, the International Federation of Air Line Pilots Associations, holding its annual conference in Auckland, New Zealand, unqualifiedly supported the stand of the American pilots. The resolution of the forty-seven member associations firmly declared that the organization would "maintain the present policy demand for one hundred and twenty nautical miles of lateral separation."

Thé FAA position was becoming increasingly untenable. Just prior to the I.C.A.O. meeting in March, 1965, the government of Canada had announced that it did not intend to support the reduced separation. A Canadian study, based on observations within the range of the Gander radar station—about two hundred miles—showed that only a reduction of not more than six nautical miles, that is, from one hundred twenty to one hundred fourteen nautical miles, would be safe. The Canadian Government declared, however, that even these results could not properly be deemed an indication for mid-ocean, where shore-based radar was unavailable, and where, consequently, track-keeping accuracy was likely to be poorer.

The British were unhappy. At this same meeting the United Kingdom submitted documents which stated that the reduction to ninety nautical miles "would clearly be unsafe." It abstained from the vote, indicating that it would have rejected the reduced separation had it been a domestic matter, but because it was an international matter, the United Kingdom would comply, "not because the required level of safety had been demonstrated, but because the North Atlantic ATS system would otherwise become unworkable."

The Air Line Pilots Association, unable to change the FAA's position, took remedial action, and presented its case to the public in an advertisement that appeared in the pages of *The New York Times* on February 24th and 25th, 1966.

The *Times* itself commented on the matter in an editorial on February 26th, 1966, saying, "As reduced airplane fares and jet speeds make air travel constantly more popular, the problem of assuring safety in crowded skies is becoming increasingly acute ... (The Federal Aviation Agency's) motivation (for narrowing the air corridors) seems plainly the pressure of air lines that want to get more planes into the limited volume of air space available during the most popular travel times ... (The pilots) fear mid-air collision because of the reduced margin for error available for planes flying near the speed of sound in the smaller corridors ... But the urgency of the pilots' words must arouse concern ... The burden of proof that the change is sound must rest upon those who, sitting safely on terra firma, have ignored the pilots' warning."

The FAA finally agreed to hold public hearings, in Washington, D.C., beginning on April 18th, 1966. The Air Line Pilots Association bought more advertising space in *The New York Times,* informing the public of the fact, and asking for continued support.

At the public hearings, the Air Line Pilots Association contended that the twenty-five percent reduction in lateral separation would greatly increase the possibilities of mid-air collision because navigational aids and techniques now in use fail to provide the precise track-keeping ability necessary.

The Association also stressed, as hard as it could, that navigational equipment and facilities, in addition to being inaccurate—for many reasons—are subject to mechanical failure. On occasion they are even subject to complete blackout.

Weather forecasting information is far from exact, moreover, and navigational techniques are subject to many vagaries. The spokesmen emphasized, above all, that *deviations from track unavoidably occur under such circumstances, no matter how expert the navigating ability of the pilot and his crew.*

It was necessary, thorough the hearings, to give the general public a clearer idea of what was at stake. An uninformed layman might think that a separation of ninety miles is safe, but an airplane need only stray forty-five miles from its lane to find itself in the air space assigned to another aircraft. As *The Air Line Pilot* said in an article on the matter in its issue of July, 1966, the situation is similar to that of an automobile crossing the median divider on a high-speed turnpike—in a fog.

Representatives of the Association repeatedly returned to the same theme: reduced separation which compresses a larger number of high-speed aircraft into the air space available greatly increases the risk of mid-air collisions, particularly when coupled with the increased and ever-increasing air traffic over the North Atlantic.

The conclusions of the Association were based on several factors. One was an analysis by systems engineering and statistical authorities of the data upon which the FAA had approved the lateral separation. *Project Accordion* was taking a beating.

Another factor was an independent survey, made by the pilots themselves, of deviations occurring in the North Atlantic. The results of this survey were vastly different from the figures presented in *Project Accordion*. It was evident that either the pilots or the FAA had erred.

A third factor did not depend on statistics. It consisted of the actual experiences of pilots—a great many pilots—with the difficulties associated with navigational deficiencies. These experiences made it plain that such deficiencies occur continually and repeatedly.

The Air Line Pilots Association representatives presented as their conclusive opinion that the data upon which the FAA relied to reduce lateral separation was, to quote *The Air Line Pilot*, "statistically distorted and biased, and it does not justify the action from a safety standpoint as it purports to do."

The representatives also concluded that deviations were actually occurring in greater numbers and were of greater magnitude than the FAA's data reflected. And they said that "the present state of the art" did not permit a reduction in lateral separation without safety risks to the public which the pilots considered unacceptable.

This stand was supported by two technical experts who had studied *Project Accordion,* Dr. Robert E. Machol, head of the Systems Engineering Department of the University of Illinois, at Chicago, and Dr. W. Edwards Deming, a consultant in statistical surveys, of Washington, D.C. It was their opinion that the data in the manner used by the FAA was "useless."

Both men insisted that the reduction would subject the traveling public to greater risks. *Project Accordion,* they declared, completely failed to justify the safety of reducing lateral separation over the North Atlantic from one hundred twenty to ninety nautical miles. They "severely criticized the report," *The Air Line Pilot* proclaimed, "as being, among other things, incomplete and inconsistent, mathematically erroneous and statistically biased."

Project Accordion, a multi-volume document running many hundreds of pages, was, Dr. Machol said, like the fairy tale emperor who believed himself dressed in his most dazzling finery, but who was actually wearing no clothes whatever. "In all of this mass of paper, *Project Accordion,*" he said, "there is nothing, correct or incorrect, which bears any pertinence to the question of flight separation errors."

A representative of the pilots dug the grave of *Project Accordian* still deeper when he presented data from their own surveys which strongly opposed a separation reduction. "Of 1,191 flights reporting in the survey," he said, "seven percent showed deviations in excess of forty-five miles."

This survey also revealed that deviations tend to occur in clusters; that is, when there is one deviation, there may be several others happening too. (The reasons for clusters were not completely clear, but the survey indicated bad weather or solar magnetic disturbances that affect the magnetic heading device.) This, obviously, made the hazard of mid-air collision still greater.

One of the pilots who testified at the hearing brought out still another point. "The horrible truth," he said, "is that all of our transatlantic aircraft are being flown primarily by the same equipment that we were using at the end of World War II—equipment that originated with two-hundred-mile-per-hour aircraft."

"There are twenty-seven carriers," the witness said, "belonging to the I.C.A.O. group of nations that are flying the North Atlantic on a regularly scheduled basis. The means that these aircraft are using to establish their position is a veritable hodge-podge of navigation equipment."

This situation, he said, was being made even more acute by the increased transatlantic traffic of privately owned jets, airplanes owned by corporations, wealthy individuals and business groups. Most of them, he declared, were equipped with navigational aids inadequate for transatlantic flights.

On April 20th, 1966, the hearings took a spectacular turn. A witness called to testify was Irving Hirsch, a former Federal Aviation Agency project supervisor, who had been in charge of the preparation of *Project Accordion for the FAA*. Hirsch, who has a master's degree in statistics, stunned most of those present when he said that the FAA survey, in his opinion, did not justify the safety aspects of the twenty-five percent reduction.

Hirsch said that the decision to reduce space over the North Atlantic had been made in the higher echelons of the FAA in Washington, removed from the technicians who prepared the report and *"without the benefit of their opinions concerning it."*

Hirsch testified that *at no time* throughout the preparation did he feel that the FAA's data supported the safety of reducing lateral separation. He said in response to questioning that he believed one hundred twenty nautical miles of lateral separation between aircraft over the North Atlantic should be restored for reasons of safety until track keeping ability of over-ocean aircraft had been improved.

He said he agreed with the testimony of previous highly-qualified witnesses who described as *useless* the FAA data used in concluding that it would be safe to reduce North Atlantic lateral separation.

The following excerpt from the actual testimony at the public hearing on April 20th is illuminating. Hirsch was being questioned by Herbert Levy, attorney for the Air Line Pilots Association.

LEVY: What was your position with the FAA?

HIRSCH: My job description was mechanical engineer.

LEVY: I see. And have you ever seen these documents, volumes one and two of Operation Accordion *before?*

108

HIRSCH: Yes, I have.

LEVY: Did you have any involvement in the preparation of these documents?

HIRSCH: Yes, I did.

LEVY: Would you describe what the nature of that involvement was, please?

HIRSCH: In Project Accordion, I was the task manager. And that responsibility involved collection of data, analysis of this data, and the presentation of the results of the program in these two volumes which, for the most part, I wrote by myself.

LEVY: I see. And is the function of the task manager in addition a supervisory function of the project?

HIRSCH: It is a supervisory position, but it was a working supervisory position.

LEVY: Thank you. Now, in the course of your studies that led you to your master's degree in statistics, did you ever hear of Dr. W. Edwards Deming?

HIRSCH: Yes, I took my master's in statistics under Dr. Deming.

LEVY: I see. And what is Dr. Deming's reputation in the field of statistics, sir? Can you tell us that?

HIRSCH: To my knowledge, Dr. Deming's expertise in statistics lies in the area of quality control, especially in the region of sampling. And he is world renowned for this type of work.

LEVY: I see. Now, Mr. Hirsch, when did you and I first meet, sir?

HIRSCH: Last evening, late.

LEVY: And have we ever talked prior to that time?

HIRSCH: I never met you before last evening.

LEVY: And, sir, did you come forward of your own volition in this matter?

HIRSCH: Yes, I certainly did.

LEVY: What prompted you to come forward?

HIRSCH: I have been following the controversy in the news-

papers, and I thought, having been so close to Project Accordion *and the separation reduction problem over the Atlantic that my testimony might be of some use to resolve the question.*

LEVY: Now, Mr. Hirsch, Drs. Deming, Machol and Roberts— and by the way, do either of the names of Machol or Roberts mean anything to you, sir?

HIRSCH: Dr. Machol I don't know personally, but I do have a volume of his book, Systems Engineering, *which I think highly of, as a matter of fact. Dr. Roberts I have heard of only through conversation with you.*

LEVY: Well, those three gentlemen, Drs. Deming, Machol and Roberts, have concluded in this proceeding after studying the two reports of Project Accordion *that these reports provide no justification for safely reducing transatlantic separation. Do you agree with that conclusion, sir?*

HIRSCH: It has always been my contention that the results of Operation Accordion *did not support the position for reduced separation to ninety nautical miles.*

LEVY: What are your views concerning the safety of the reduced separation, sir?

HIRSCH: I think the factual evidence of large error data as collected under the auspices of Accordion *would be the strongest evidence against the position for reduced separation.*

LEVY: Now, Mr. Hirsch, do you know of any documentation containing the reasons why the reduced separation standard received the approval of the FAA?

HIRSCH: This I cannot say. I can say that the decision was made in Washington pretty much removed from the technical area where the facts were gathered.

Perhaps even more significant than the above testimony is an earlier wire from Irving Hirsch to Herbert Levy. Mr. Hirsch probed beyond the report to say that *Operation Accordion* cast doubt on the FAA position on reducing the lateral separation.

Hirsch disclosed an additional alarming point: 3.4 transatlantic civil jet flights out of every 100 strayed from planned course 40 nautical miles or more (up to a maximum of 90 nautical miles).

But the final shock came to me when an official spokesman for the airlines declared at the hearing that the individual pilot was not in a position to evaluate the relative safety aspects of the narrower corridor!

The pilots, both American and foreign, continued their fight, making all available information public. For a time it appeared that the hearings would be resumed in June, but on June 6th the FAA announced they were being postponed. No date was given for their resumption, and the pilots, still doing battle for the cause of safety, dug in for a long, hard campaign.

Then, unexpectedly, on June 10th, 1966, just as traffic across the Atlantic was soaring toward its summer peak, all four governments and the FAA changed their stand.

It was announced that a corridor of one hundred twenty nautical miles of lateral separation would be restored as of June 12th. *Project Accordion* was buried without honor.

The pilots view their success on this question as a major victory for aviation and the flying public. *The Air Line Pilot* said in its July 1966 issue, "It is an example of recognition of a problem by the Association, with corresponding action to avert tragedy *before* an accident occurs, rather than cleaning up a dangerous situation *after* an accident."

In the words of Capt. Ruby, the Air Line Pilots Association president, "There has never been a collision between two airliners flying over the Atlantic. We aim to keep it that way."

The problem that caused the preparation and implementation of *Project Accordion* remains, however. Air traffic over the North Atlantic continues to grow, and the demand for seating space at the most desired hours during the rush season are difficult to obtain. What can and should be done?

I've been told that various plans are being formulated for the making of new surveys. Not only are such reports useless, but they are also wasteful of large sums of money. The only real solution to the North Atlantic traffic problem is the development and required use of precise navigational aids that will, eventually, permit the reduction of lateral corridors. There is no other way.

I take great personal pride in being a member of the organization that entered the battle with long odds against it (big business, the U.S. Government, and several foreign governments) *and won*.

The pilots were waging a war for the sake of safety, nothing else. We were fighting for a principle: There can be no "short-cuts" to safe flying.

IX

AIRPORTS: SAFETY HAZARDS IN THE JET AGE

A fellow pilot who is a close friend calls many American airports "postage stamps," and he doesn't smile when he says it. There are few airports which pilots accept without qualification. Since the reader now realizes the importance of take-offs and landings, and knows that ninety percent of all accidents take place then, the importance of superior facilities for those phases is obvious. *Too often the facilities are not even adequate!*

Let's first examine the background of airports—how they grew. When the aviation industry was a struggling infant and money was scarce, airports were bedraggled orphans. Many were located in areas, usually on the outskirts of a city or town, that no one else wanted. It didn't matter if the site was located close to gas storage tanks, power lines and transmitter towers. There might be natural or man-made obstacles in the vicinity, but the airport builders couldn't afford to pick and choose, and the old barnstorming pilots were happy to have a place—*any* place—to take off and land.

The old-time pilot learned to live with hazards, and the airport designers and city planners who stepped into the picture when the industry began to prosper took it for granted that the aviation industry could make itself at home anywhere. It has, because there has been no choice.

113

In the days of propeller planes, it was *relatively* easy to get along with what we were given. Those days are behind us. *In to-day's jet age, inadequate airport facilities constitute an ever present hazard to safety, and will continue to do so until an aroused public demands that the local authority and the Federal Aviation Agency use higher, uniform standards.*

There is an urgent need for:

1. Longer runways and with safe overrun areas to accommodate jets.
2. Better obstruction and runway lights.
3. Improved electronic instrument landing systems.
4. Elimination of ditches and ridges adjacent to runways.
5. Elimination of dangerous obstructions in the vicinity of airports.
6. The provision of adequate airport fire-fighting and rescue equipment.

Too often all but the largest airports (which are themselves far from perfect) are second-rate. Too often these smaller airports have only one runway that jets can use, and under certain wind and weather conditions, the margin of safety shrinks to the vanishing point.

In general the problem is money. The cost of providing adequate safety margins at all airports is substantial. Therefore, the public must make the final decision. If you want safe airports, you must take appropriate action through your municipal, state and federal representatives. Neither the pilots nor the airlines who employ us can do it for you.

The greatest single need, in the opinion of pilots, is longer runways. When a pilot approaches a short runway, particularly in bad weather, he is flirting with danger. When he takes off from a short runway, particularly when there are obstructions in the vicinity of the airport and an emergency develops, he is taking his life—and your life—in his hands.

A note about runway length and tailwinds. The maximum permissible factor is 10 knots in a vector directly from the stern.

This is equivalent to approximately 1200 feet of runway length at our normal landing speed.

Thus, an 8,000-foot runway could become 6,800 feet of effective runway.

This factor must be computed for every airport, lest safe-length runways become marginal ... or marginal ones, unusable.

The problem was discussed at length in two articles which appeared in the *Air Line Pilot Magazine* in its issues of September, 1964, and August, 1965, and were reprinted in a special pamphlet in November, 1965. This monthly publication of the Air Line Pilots Association declared, in part:

"When overrun accidents occur during landing or accelerate-stop, aborted take-offs, the blame should be placed on shoulders other than the pilot's."

This is the opinion ALPA expressed to the Federal Aviation Agency in a letter written following a recent public hearing on "Notice of Proposed Rule Making 63-28" on amendments to Special Regulations relating to accelerate-stop and landing distances for turbojet category airplanes. The letter was prompted by testimony submitted by some major segments of the industry in opposition to increasing the required runway lengths for wet or slippery conditions.

"NASA and the FAA have justifiably seen fit to spend huge sums on research to learn more about realistic requirements for runway lengths to assure an adequate margin of safety for scheduled aircraft operations during slippery runway conditions," ALPA said in its letter. "The data has been obtained and the results are clear." The FAA, CAB and NASA have gone on record stating that our runway lengths are deficient for scheduled air carrier operations.

The letter continued to say that the Association representatives spearheading these studies for ALPA have often pointed out the inadequacy of runway lengths for landing and take-off during slippery conditions.

"These inadequacies are due to obsolete certification require-

115

ments which are not commensurate with operational experience," ALPA stressed, adding that in view of the research and testing which has been conducted, overrun and underrun accidents can no longer be tolerated.

"In the design of the airplane," the letter continued, "we provide margins for structure and redundancy in systems to prevent accidents, yet we fail to provide comparable margins of runway length. By the record this dereliction has resulted in a terrible loss of life, injury and damage to property. It has detracted from the profitable operation of the carriers and continues to adversely affect the safety and economical growth of air carrier operations. Surely, aviation has reached a stature, particularly in air carrier operations, in which the lack of adequate airport safety margins should not be a continued cause for the same type of accidents to occur year after year."

[Note: All too often these accidents are erroneously labeled "Pilot Error."]

Concluding, ALPA told the FAA Administrator, "Knowing of your familiarity with the subject matter, it seems pointless to go on further, other than to restate and belabor the point that penalizing the pilot for an overrun accident, if he survives, is not the answer nor is it in the best interest of the public. We, therefore, respectfully request that you exert the power of your office in consonance with the intent of the Federal Aviation Act of 1958, to remedy this condition by providing adequate runway length margins for the maximum safety during operation of air line aircraft. It is realized our airports cannot be updated to meet new runway length requirements overnight. However a realistic time schedule, similar to the vigorous and ruthless highway program, should be established to obtain a level of safety the air traveling public is entitled to have."

The Association emphasizes that no one more than the pilot is striving to accomplish as safe a landing as is humanly possible and the safety record is good in this regard except when the slippery runway conditions exist. Then, longer runways are needed

116

at certain airports. It is not the Association's objective to recommend off-loading or any economic restriction in the load carrying ability of the airplane as a method of solving the runway length problem.

Let me point out that the position of the Air Line Pilots Association has been based on the actual experience in take-off and landings of professional air line pilots who have made *millions*—to be more specific, four million take-offs and four million landings per year!

Following the appearance of this first article, a new Federal Aviation Regulations amendment provided for a fifteen percent increase in the effective runway length requirement for turbojet aircraft landing on a wet surface. Directly after this, a Continental Airlines Boeing 707, carrying fifty-nine passengers and a crew of seven, crashed at the end of its landing roll on a rain-slick seven thousand foot runway at the Kansas City, Missouri, Municipal Airport. Only the skill of the pilot combined with good fortune, made it possible for the airplane to come to a halt safely, without fatalities, after striking a dike sideways.

The Air Line Pilots Association believes that the new amendment is an *interim* step in the right direction, but that *it still does not provide the public with the safety margin it deserves when using air service.* The Association also feels that, as has so often been true in other aspects of regulating safe operations, facilities and equipment, too much time elapsed in obtaining the rule.

I feel, as does every other pilot I know, that airport safety margins have not kept pace with the jet plane and its high speed performance.

Before leaving the subject of runway length I want to clarify what we pilots mean by the term "marginal". Basically, a longer runway is a better runway. But as you will see on the following pages where I "score" United States airports which handle jet airplanes, a shorter runway may be workable for its particular traffic, and a longer runway may still not be workable enough.

A runway must be right for the missions of any and all airplanes which can reasonably be expected to use it. And while the average airline passenger may feel that his flight is a standard mission it is obvious that missions can really be classified in quite different categories.

East and West Coast airports, for example, can expect to send off and receive non-stop flights from across the continent and from overseas. Large, long-range 4-engine jets require long runways. These jets must accelerate 300,000 or more pounds to approximately 200 miles per hour in order to become airborne. Medium-range jets, the lighter weight 4-engine and 3-engine airplanes can accommodate themselves on shorter runways, and finally, the short-range 2-engine jets can use still shorter runways.

Please note that just as different airplanes have their particular "empty weights," the very same airplane may vary its gross weight from take-off to take-off by well over one hundred thousand pounds, by a variance in the revenue load and in the fuel load. Thus a runway that was suitable for a certain plane on a certain take-off may be marginal for that same plane on another take-off . . . or completely unusable. Airplane weight is, in fact, the most important factor in determining the safety element of a runway.

An additional factor that affects the amount of runway needed is the altitude of the airport. Cities such as Denver, Colorado and Albuquerque, New Mexico, whose airports are approximately one mile high, need additional runway lengths.

Again, airplanes are capable of taking off and landing in shorter distances in cold weather. Hot climates or high temperatures introduce another runway length factor.

Obstructions—hills, mountains, man-made structures—also count in these determinations. And of course weather—precipitation, wind, water, snow or ice—all present problems of varying degrees in the factor of safe runway length.

Even the electronic and visual aids for the pilot who is trying to locate the runway affect the amount of runway he will use in his landing, since the approach cannot begin until he is certain of his location.

In two words, the "margin" that we pilots are concerned about is the *safety margin*.

In addition to design factors and safety margins, there is, of course, the human element.

Consider the individual who gives the pilot his runway assignment in the first place. This happens to be an FAA personage, the tower operator.

Here is how one tower operator's judgment deprived a pilot of his valuable safety margins during a recent landing at O'Hare Airport, Chicago.

Chicago O'Hare is presently in the process of lengthening Runway 13 left and 31 right. Of course, the construction area at the end of the usable runway is marked by flags and lights. The FAA issued NOTAMS (notices to airmen) advising pilots of this construction work. All this makes it completely legal. Nevertheless, there is still only 6300 feet of usable runway remaining. For the larger jets, this is marginal and, of course, when adverse conditions are added, the safety margin decreases.

Recently, a flight was cleared to land on this particular short runway. The pilot requested permission to use the parallel or longer runway. He was advised by the tower that he would have an hour delay if he chose to use the longer runway. The weather was clear, and as far as a passenger could tell, all conditions were perfect. The plane was a large 4-engine jet and was heavily loaded. All of these factors made the longer runway more desirable. Under these conditions, an hour delay would have been difficult to explain to a passenger who missed his connection in Chicago that day, and O'Hare handles more connecting passengers than any other airport. Although the pilot realized that he would be placed in a compromising situation, he acceded and landed on the shorter runway. Ironically, at the very same time, a lighter weight 3-engine jet which requires considerably less runway was

119

landing on the longer runway. Directing the larger and faster jet for a landing on the longer runway would have required a little extra effort on the part of the air traffic controllers. They chose the easy way and placed the additional burden on the pilot. Situations such as this occur frequently throughout the United States.

As a footnote to human judgment, let me criticize the legal bickering that can sometimes lead to danger. This is the latest development in the unfortunate LaGuardia Airport story. Due to noise problems, the Port of New York Authority closed Runway 4 for landing use and Runway 22 for take-offs. Recently, the FAA opened these runways for use. As soon as airline operators started using the runways, the Port Authority obtained a court order enjoining them from further use. Lately, this injunction has been upheld in a federal district court. While this legal controversy continues, pilots are doing their best to make safe landings and take-offs. Many times, the weather is poor at LaGuardia and restrictions to a crosswind or downwind landing or take-off only aggravate the situation. Until such time as all construction is completed and the runways are made usable, I suggest that LaGuardia be closed for all operations.

In the "good old days," then, when airports were located on the outskirts of cities, and were easily identified, airplanes were slower, and pilots, particularly the airline pilots who flew their routes regularly, knew all the landmarks of the approach paths to every runway at every airport they used regularly. Those days are gone. In fact, a regulation of the old Civil Aviation Authority, the predecessor of the FAA, reads like ancient history: "A pilot shall not descend below his minimum approach altitude until he has the runway, runway lights or objects identifiable therewith in sight."

Cities have grown, and are growing. The bare fields have given way to housing and industrial developments, suburbs have mushroomed, and frequently airports are surrounded by heavily populated areas. With the advent of television, high towers sprang up, seemingly out of nowhere. Airplane traffic increased, and continues to increase. Airplanes grew larger and faster.

Then came the jet! The old problems multiplied, and new ones were created. Air traffic control problems became acute, and continue to deteriorate. At our busiest airports, today, in perfect weather, an airplane may be forced to wait an hour or more to land or take off. The speeds of airplanes using the same air space in the vicinity of airports varies sharply. For example, some of our more modern jets are required to maintain up to twice the speed of lighter airplanes in traffic patterns.

However, I don't want to give the impression that we have nothing but ever worsening headaches. There *have* been improvements, many of them. Radar has been tremendously helpful in handling traffic in and out of airports. The ILS—Instrument Landing System—has been improved and installed at virtually all major airports; two or more are available at some of our larger and busier airports.

Other approach aids have been installed, too, among them the Visual Glide Slope, which consists of two sets of lights installed near the approach end of a runway. Each unit consists of a set of white lights and another of red lights which cast their beams up the approach line to a runway. As the airplane is aligned with the runway and moves into the right "approach slot," the pilot sees an amber beam, created by a mixture of the white and the red. If the pilot descends too low in the slot, the red becomes increasingly pronounced, indicating that he should descend at a slower rate. If the airplane is too high, all he sees is white, which indicates that he should descend more rapidly.

The Visual Glide Slope is not an expensive installation, and I wish more airports used it—does yours? It is a valuable approach aid, particularly at night, when visibility may be restricted by snow, rain, smog, fog, smoke, haze, and so on.

I must, in all fairness, mention other aids which are helpful: the REIL (runway end identification lights), two flashing white lights located at the end of a runway; touch-down zone lights, which identify this area; center-line runway lights, which help a pilot keep his airplane aligned and are of assistance in attaining depth perception at night.

Now, let's look back at the other side of the coin. The reader may be surprised to learn that runways are often rough, which is a cause of real concern. A rough runway creates a distortion of the wings, thus reducing lift when they are heavily loaded. The different textures of runways affect the braking capacities of an airplane, and a pilot must be alert to them at all times. Asphalt, of course, becomes soft on very hot days, which also makes it more difficult to accelerate.

The lack of overrun areas is surprising: the simple installation of one thousand to two thousand feet of plain sand at the ends of runways could prevent many overshoot accidents.

The aviation industry has been pushing to the limit the maximum allowable gross weight in order to carry more payload a greater distance. As a result, many airports with insufficient runway lengths are outdated. *Too many airports do not have runways of sufficient length to enable pilots to operate with adequate safety margins under ALL operating conditions.* I cannot stress this point too strongly.

There is no perfect airport anywhere, I suppose. But, as a pilot who flies the transatlantic run every week, I appreciate the London Airport. Until something better is built, this is my favorite anywhere. It has a splendid lighting system (made necessary by London's fogs) and the lights work magnificently. It also has a good instrument approach system relatively free of obstructions. Control tower personnel are always alert, crisp, professional and courteous. "Unflappable," as they say.

I must admit that Londoners don't care for the roar of jets any more than do the people of other cities, so there are noise abatement procedures at London Airport that make me uneasy. Pilots are forced to live with these procedures everywhere.

One of the biggest problems at airports for those engaged in international flying is the language barrier. English is the international language when a pilot flies from one country to another, regardless of the nationality of either. (For example, a French pilot landing at an Italian airport converses in English with the control tower. A Greek pilot and an Egyptian ground control operator speak English.) But something can be lost in translation, particularly when there is an emergency. Even the best of control tower personnel and the most experienced pilots tend to revert to their native tongues at such times. I know of no accidents caused by language differences, but, to my knowledge, there have been a number of near misses. In anything other than a normal landing or take-off situation, when an airport traffic control operator needs to relay specific, other-than-routine instructions, the chance of a misunderstanding increases.

The airlines are well aware of these problems, and act accordingly to reduce risks. For example, one foreign carrier has a policy requiring a pilot who understands and speaks English fluently to fly as a third pilot *for three years* on flights to the United States before he is allowed to assume full responsibility for accepting clearances and other traffic instructions. Other foreign carriers have similar policies.

Flight 800
Smoking wreckage at Fiumicino Airport.

Design Error

Wreckage of EAL Electra is raised in Boston Harbor. Birds were blamed for this accident. But was the Electra basically unsafe? It was never grounded...but quick modifications were made.

Hydroplaning

At 80 knots (1) a wave of slush is thrown up, at 120 knots (2) the nose-wheel is hydroplaning, at 135 knots (3) there is no direct tire-to-runway contact. A serious problem, the cause of many overshoots, hydroplaning has not yet been solved.

Fire

Causes of death: burns, and the inhalation of fire and smoke. Inadequate fire-fighting equipment and rescue procedures at Stapleton Field were criticized when this UAL DC-8 crashed on July 11th, 1961.

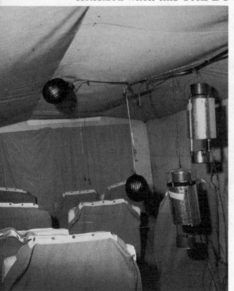

Before-and-after effects of fire in the cabin of an "average airliner." (*ALPA tests*)

Congestion

The December 16th, 1960 tragedy over New York City came just four days after a warning by the Executive Director of the Air Traffic Control Association. In notable subsequent litigation, the courts differed from the CAB's probable cause finding, and in my own opinion the basic cause was an antiquated air traffic controls system.

"Operation Accordion"

Author (center, standing) went to Washington on the ALPA team for the sensational safety battle over the

Zoning

Contractors still receive permits to build homes next to airport fences... ...and planes still fall into residential areas during take-offs and approaches to airports. Dallas, Texas: Plane just a few feet above a busy highway on a runway approach of an improperly planned and zoned airport.

"Probable Cause"

Accident investigators confer at a crash site...and
...in New York City's Federal Building.

'Probable Cause"

Wreckage is pieced together in a search for the probable cause.
The torn and crumpled metallic tape of this flight recorder is one hope
of determining the cause.

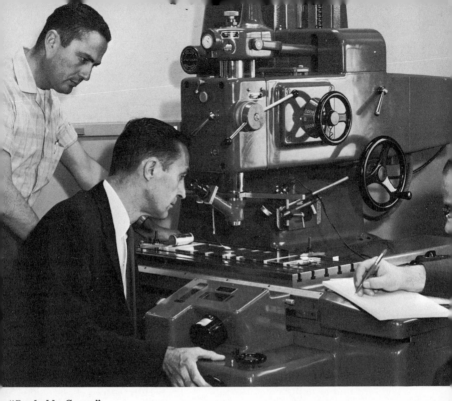

"Probable Cause"

James A. Furr, ALPA, with John Pahl and Edward Patton, CAB, at the National Bureau of Standards during a tape read-out session. Graph plotted from the read-out of a scheduled Caravelle trip indicates the rapid onset of severe turbulence.

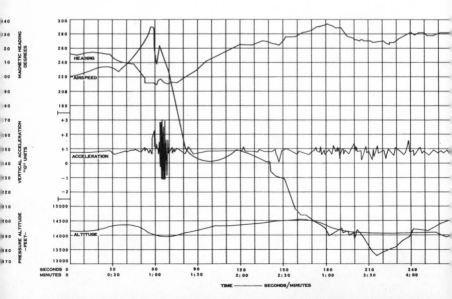

Marginal Runways

A Pan American airliner...a foggy night...another overrun accident. The pilot of a 707 aborted take-off at O'Hare International, returned to the runway and taxied back to the terminal. Without sufficient level terrain, there could have been another tragedy.

Marginal Runways

ALPA had declared this 7,000-foot runway at Kansas City Municipal too short for adverse-weather jet operation. Yet the runway was legally open when this Continental 707 landed in heavy rain the morning of July 1st, 1965. It skidded through a fence, sliced through radar buildings, and broke up as it went over the dike, just short of the Missouri River.

Weather

Inaccurate weather information contributed to the crash of this American airliner in New York City's East River. There was also an obsolete altimeter. As usual, "pilot error" was implied.

The "T-Tailed Tigress"

Chocolate brown with canary yellow markings, the first Boeing 727 rolls out of its Renton, Washington factory and...takes off.

The gutted UAL 727 which crashed at Salt Lake City. *(See Chapter XIV)*

X

A SURVEY OF AMERICAN AIRPORTS

For the past two years I have been making a personal, airport-by-airport survey in the United States. The criterion has been operational safety, not de luxe baggage systems, nor decor in passenger lounges. Seriously, I hope that you will insist, with me, that "your" money be spent for safety first, always. Let me hasten to make it clear that, since I am now on the transatlantic run to Europe and the Middle East, I have scrupulously corroborated my facts with a most reliable "team" of airline pilot colleagues now on the domestic runs. In each instance, when we developed a report that was other than good, still another pilot double-checked it, and only if he concurred have I included that material here.

As a prelude, let me emphasize that in general the United States has the best airports and equipment, as befits the wealthiest and most air-minded nation. When an American airport is good, it is very good ... but when an American airport is inferior, it is all the more flagrant a disregard for the safety of our citizens who use its facilities.

Limitations of space in these pages, and of the time of the pilots who have worked with me, have made it impossible to include all airports in the United States used by jet airplanes. Therefore

I must beg the indulgence of readers whose cities may have been omitted; no slight has been intended.

Cities are presented in a "pilot's" rather than a "reader's" order, but I do want to start with the best.

WASHINGTON D.C.

Dulles Airport

In my opinion Dulles Airport is the safest, finest airport in the United States. It has two parallel, widely separated north-south runways, and another that runs northwest-southeast. All are made of light-colored concrete, which helps a pilot in landings. Depth perception at night is good, and the runways are far less slippery, when wet, than black-top.

Each of the runways has its own, complete ILS system, together with all of the associated light systems; there are high intensity approach lights, strobe flashing lights, variable intensity touch-down lights, and center line lights. It has high speed turn-offs into taxi-ways, excellent taxi-ways, and the ramp areas are well lighted and marked. It is virtually free of obstructions, both at the field itself and in the vicinity.

I enjoy using it, and so do other pilots. We wish it could be used as a model for the rebuilding of other American airports. Ironically, it has the lightest traffic of any major airport in the United States. It is located rather far from the center of the city, and passengers who are in a hurry (almost all passengers are in a hurry) find it inconvenient.

National Airport

The runways are very short, but the airport is convenient; passengers can reach the center of Washington quickly. From the standpoint of safety, there is no comparison possible. Because of the insistent passenger demand, the scheduled airline carriers clamor for the use of National, which creates traffic hazards.

Noise abatement procedures create problems.

This "downtown" airport, located on the west bank of the Po-

126

tomac River, is completely surrounded by the city, which means pilots face "obstacle courses" on take-offs and landings, and approach patterns must snake along the Potomac.

It was opened to jets only recently, and due to short runways, the bigger jets seldom use it. Traffic is limited to two- and three-engine jets.

National does have an ILS system with associated lights to the north. But to the south there are only runway end identification lights. The runway length is marginal (6870 feet), and requires a turn-in at a low altitude so the pilot can align with the runway.

I've been told that National is a profitable operation, but that Dulles loses money . . .

CHICAGO, ILLINOIS

O'Hare Airport

Chicago was once the busiest railroad center in the world. O'Hare is now the world's busiest airport.

Traffic congestion is so great and so hectic that when a pilot receives his airway traffic control, taxi or take-off clearance, he is frequently unable to confirm that clearance. In normal radio procedures, a pilot repeats clearance to make certain he has understood every detail clearly. At O'Hare, because of the traffic congestion, there just isn't time.

Control tower operators are forced to rip out clearances in a steady, unending stream. If United Airlines Flight 100 and American Airlines Flight 100 are both waiting for clearance to land, the pilots must be on their toes; should a message become slightly garbled, neither is quite certain whether it is he who has been cleared to land.

A pilot may be a mile or two from the end of the runway, and after the tower gives him clearance to land, the instructions continue to pour out to other airplanes. At the same time, one or two other airplanes may be receiving take-off clearances on this same runway.

Chicago has its share of weather. Ceilings are often low, and consequently visibility may be poor. As a result of the traffic congestion, combined with the poor visibility, a pilot frequently is unable to see another airplane on the runway, so he comes in without a feeling of confidence that the runway has been cleared for him.

O'Hare is located in an area where wind conditions may be extreme, even for Chicago. It is not unusual to encounter gusts and strong winds that blow at acute angles to the runways. And the runways are often slippery due to rain, snow or ice.

Snowbanks and other obstructions near runways present dangerous hazards. Should trouble develop on take-off, such as the failure of an outboard engine, an airplane tends to swerve toward these obstructions.

Let me cite a personal experience at O'Hare. On a typical day, back in 1963, the wind was blowing at sixty miles per hour from the southwest, directly down the southwest runway. Since this runway was only 6000 feet long (it is now 7500 feet), it was not approved for take-off use by 707 jets. However, under the weather conditions that were prevailing, take-off from an east-west runway was legal.

Theoretically, I had two choices. I could take off on an approved runway with an extreme crosswind, which was legal, or I could make a faster, safer take-off into the wind on an illegal runway. In reality, I had no choice. If I was to fly, I had to take off on the east-west runway. I complied with regulations, but in my opinion I was taking substantially more risk; a mechanical malfunction could have resulted in a serious situation.

When there is a strong crosswind, an airplane tends to "weathercock" into it. To prevent this and keep his airplane on the runway, a pilot must be particularly alert. Any failure that diverts his attention from the controls for a second might cause his airplane to veer off the runway.

Another experience at O'Hare comes to mind. One day I had a student flight engineer on board, whose work was being supervised by a check-flight engineer. Following normal procedures, we started our engines and taxied out. The student engineer forgot to turn off the fuel pump switch on the number one fuel tank pump, which permitted the fuel to flow from the number one tank on the left side of the airplane through a cross-feed line to the number four tank on the right side of the airplane. So, during the taxi run, several thousand pounds of fuel flowed from one side of the airplane to the other.

The only fuel quantity gauges showing the amount of fuel in each tank are located on the flight engineer's panel, and neither the check-flight engineer nor the student noticed the discrepancy.

During the critical portion of my take-off run, when I was travelling approximately one hundred miles per hour, I realized that something was seriously amiss: the right side of my aircraft was sagging, and the ship showed a strong tendency to veer to the right.

The runway, typical of O'Hare in winter, had large areas which were completely ice-covered and very slippery.

I suspected landing gear trouble (broken tires, etc.) but couldn't identify the cause of my problem, and had literally one to two seconds in which to make a decision. I could either try to abort the take-off on the icy runway, or make the take-off with this baffling flight characteristic.

I elected to continue the take-off.

As I lifted off, the right wing displayed a strong tendency to drop. I struggled with the airplane until I gained a little altitude. At this point I recognized the problem, and corrected it by cross-feeding the fuel from the number four tank to all the engines. I had no further trouble.

Had I aborted the take-off on that ice-covered runway, there well might have been a disaster. Please understand that I'm not blaming O'Hare for Chicago's weather. But I wished—and still wish—that the runway had been longer, and that something had been done to clear the runway of ice before take-offs were permitted.

O'Hare has an ILS on every runway except the northeast-southwest, and the southwest has a visual glide slope, which makes it the best for instrument approaches.

Except for the southeast-northwest runway, the runways are marginal in length.

The associated lighting systems are only fair. They lack center line lights and touch-down zone lights.

Because of the exceptionally heavy traffic at O'Hare, I believe that *all* electronic, mechanical and other aids should be utilized.

KANSAS CITY, MISSOURI

Municipal Airport

Four simple words, "Kansas City Municipal Airport," are enough to make any jet pilot shudder. There may be a worse jet airport somewhere in the world, but I haven't had the misfortune to discover it.

My opinion is not mine alone. The citizens of Kansas City recognized their need, and a group called the Kansas Citians for a Greater Kansas City is working on a drive—with the whole-hearted cooperation of the pilots—to raise six million dollars for the construction of a new facility, to be known as the Mid-Continent Airport. In a brochure describing the present abomination this group said, "Our outmoded, one-runway airport is totally unsuited for the Jet Age. It is surrounded by rivers, high buildings and railways, and has the least desirable safe landing limits of any city in the United States. These conditions cannot be improved, due to the elevation of the field and the height of the buildings and other obstructions around it."

The *Air Line Pilot* has also used the moderate language of temperate men in discussing Municipal Airport, saying, "Overruns are caused initially by one or more of a number of unavoidable (and usually compounded) conditions—slippery runways, worn, smooth tires, crosswinds and high or fast approaches due to adverse weather—but the causal factor underlying all overrun crack-ups is the fact that most runways are *too short* for operations under those conditions!

"An overrun on landing is not the only situation in which tragedy lurks on a short runway. A great danger of overrun exists in the case of an aborted take-off, especially during hot weather or on icy or slushy runway surfaces (both are frequent conditions at Kansas City Municipal Airport). It is extremely doubtful whether a jet-liner pilot could stop his aircraft before the end of a seven thousand foot runway (even a dry one) if he were to experience a power failure at or near V-1, the speed at which he must decide whether to continue the take-off or abort."

Let me fill in a few details. The one runway is short. There are dikes at both ends, and obstructions all around. For all practical purposes, the airport is located in the heart of the city.

A pilot who wants thrills, or is trying to demonstrate his skills, may do so by landing north in Kansas City when it is snowing or raining. The instrument landing approach is from the north, and as he breaks out of the overcast and spots the ground, he circles the airport, flying just a few hundred feet above buildings and smokestacks. During this time, of course, he must, as he peers through the precipitation, try to keep the runway in sight.

As he turns north and aligns his airplane with the runway, he must clear a major obstacle, the smoke stacks atop Rudy's Seed Factory. Then, descending with very precise speed and altitude control (still looking out of his window through the rain or snow), he must make certain his wheels clear the Kaw River dike.

It is essential that he set his airplane down as close to the beginning of the slippery runway as possible, of course, so he can manage to stop before the dike at the far end.

If you think I feel strongly on the subject, you're right! You see, my first year of jet flying was spent on a run between New York and Kansas City. In 1961 I wrote a letter vehemently protesting the use of the Kansas City Municipal Airport for jet

131

operations. Many other jet pilots have done the same, but the airport is still in operation, and the toll of accidents continues to mount. Two of my friends have had accidents there ... with their "Probable Cause" reports showing an almost unbelievable analysis of "Pilot Error!"

BOSTON, MASS.

Logan Field

Theoretically, Logan Field, Boston, is an ideal airport. The instrument approach runway to the northeast is a superb 10,023 feet in length, and has approach lights, sequence flasher and high intensity runway lights. Sounds good, doesn't it?

Well, we pilots have long been recommending, urging and all but begging that Logan be *abandoned* as a jet airport, and that another, more suitable airport be built somewhere in the Boston area. Logan is marginally safe at best.

Because of ships moving in and out of Boston Harbor, the glide slope intercepts the runway 3500 feet from the threshold, leaving only 6523 feet of remaining runway, which is dangerously inadequate under adverse weather conditions. Only if the weather is fine, with a ceiling of one thousand feet and visibility of three miles, do you get to use the full length of the runway. At such times, of course, the full length is least needed.

A jet pilot's heart really sinks when he comes into Logan and sees, or is told by ground control, that an aircraft carrier is anchored in the harbor. I'm an admirer of the United States Navy and of the young men who fly from the decks, but at such times my thoughts are unprintable. You must change from your normal approach path and come in much higher, which means land farther down the runway, and have still less room to bring yourself to a stop.

The other runways are marginal in length, without exception.

Approach aids are inadequate, except on the northwest runway, which has approach lights and an ILS system. The runway itself is only 7883 feet in length, however, which is marginal for all-weather operations.

It is virtually impossible to expand this airport or lengthen the runways. Approaches to Logan are obstructed by large buildings, and the runways terminate in Boston Harbor, so it would be economically unfeasible to extend the runways to the lengths pilots believe necessary to provide an adequate margin of safety.

I'm not speaking slang when I say that this airport is for the birds. Birds are a major problem in the area. The reader may recall that birds were held responsible for the crash of an Eastern Airlines Lockheed Electra in Boston, just after it had taken off. Every pilot is apprehensive that gulls or other birds will be sucked into his aircraft's engines at Logan.

Various official notices to pilots tell us to "beware" of birds. I'm a cautious man, conscious of my responsibilities. But I'm sorry to say, I've never been able to figure out just what this means.

When taking off or landing at Logan in foggy, wet weather, a flock of seagulls suddenly rises in front of my airplane. I "beware" of them all right, but there they are. How could I have avoided them? What do I do now? Nobody has yet told me.

NEW YORK CITY

John F. Kennedy Airport

As recently as 1950, Kennedy Airport fulfilled its original name, and was both idle and wild. How times have changed! Cutterhead dredges throw sand onto marshland near the airport, and before the sand is dry, real estate men are building new housing developments, thereby laying the foundations of new noise abatement programs and problems.

JFK, the great international airport of America's first city, should be a model. It isn't.

It is one of the busiest airports in the world. Of the many runways, four of them will accommodate jets, no matter what the wind directions. However, due to noise abatement procedures and obstructions, pilots are not permitted to use all four runways at all times, nor to utilize the full lengths of these runways.

I fly in and out of Kennedy regularly, and often feel frustrated about their long, safe runways.

The criteria applied to runway number four, the primary instrument landing runway, are applied to other runways as well, including those better able to handle four-engine jets. Extensions have been built onto two runways, but, due to the noise abatement program, these extensions are not fully utilized.

Mechanical, electronic and other aids at this airport are first-rate, but the traffic is so severe that on November 2nd, 1966 Oscar Bakke, regional FAA director, warned that all international flights might have to be diverted as a "possible avenue of relief." (He blamed "local authorities" for the problem . . .)

LaGuardia Airport

This has always been a problem airport, and has had a long history of accidents. One of the most spectacular occurred when a runway had been shortened, due to construction work. (It seems there is almost always construction work of some kind going on there.) An American Airlines Lockheed Electra hit a poorly marked dike, flipped over and slid, upside down. Fortunately, it did not catch fire, and passengers were able to escape from the wreckage.

Pilots have been battling for greater safety at LaGuardia, fighting the New York Port Authority and badgering the FAA. There are obstructions everywhere, and virtually every approach to the airport has some bad features. During many periods of construction work, when tall cranes and other equipment were on the fields and trucks were moving across runways, pilots just threatened to stop flying in and out of the field unless the equipment was removed, and pilots have been known to reject the runways assigned them for take-offs.

All runways are short.

This problem is further complicated by the noise abatement

program. Citizens who live near LaGuardia complain constantly about jet noises, and I certainly can't blame them. But the noise abatement procedures instituted to placate them seriously compromise safety.

After a pilot lands on runway number twenty-two, for example, he approaches an end which quite literally terminates a few feet short of Grand Central Parkway, a major automobile thoroughfare. On one occasion an airplane actually overshot the end of the runway and found itself on the parkway, endangering the lives of motorists as well as the passengers in the airplane.

Obstructions in the vicinity create frightful hazards. Under normal operating conditions a pilot flies well above these obstructions, but if he loses an engine on a take-off he's in trouble. The obstacles range from the Bronx-Whitestone Bridge to a body of water at one end of the field, not to mention the Triborough Bridge, the skyscrapers of Manhattan and the smokestacks, towers and tanks of Queens.

The approach to runway number twenty-two has not improved over the years. It still looks like a black hole, particularly at night. Also, the approach lights to this runway are mounted on steel towers, creating a nasty hazard.

The approach to runway number thirteen is another nightmare. Consolidated Edison's, five old, smoky stacks must be cleared.

On three approaches to runways, there are dikes that must be cleared before a pilot touches down.

The new runway extension at LaGuardia is on firm ground, I'm delighted to say. The rest of the airport, located on marshland, is sinking; I've been told the rate is six to ten inches per year . . .

HOUSTON, TEXAS

Hobby Airport
This old airport is located very near to the many petroleum

refineries in Baytown and Bayport. Unfortunately, the prevailing winds cause thick industrial smoke to drift over the airport. Consequently, the field often must be closed during the early morning hours at some seasons of the year because of smoke, fog and smog. Visibility is reduced when the wind is blowing from east-southeast.

The runways are slightly more than seven thousand feet in length, and are marginal. However, they are relatively clear of obstructions.

International Jetero Airport

This new field is north of Houston, approximately twenty miles from the industrial area, so smoke and smog should create less of a problem here.

I understand that this field will be a real model, with long runways and excellent approach aids, as well as few obstructions. When Texans go to town, they really shoot the works! I'm anxious to see this field.

SAN ANTONIO, TEXAS

San Antonio International

The countryside is flat, which is helpful to both take-offs and landings. Approach facilities are good. The biggest obstacles are natural: stratus clouds and fog are prevalent.

DALLAS, TEXAS

Love Field

The longest runway is 8800 feet. The radio aids, ILS, marker beacons and related landing aids are excellent. The runways are good for medium-haul and short-haul jets, but safety is marginal for long-haul jets.

One approach lies over the heart of the city, where tall buildings create hazards.

There are noise abatement problems at the airport.

At the Ross Avenue intersection, there is an obstruction 1095 feet high. (I might add that the elevation of the airport itself is 485 feet.)

FORT WORTH, TEXAS

Greater Southwest International

The approaches are reasonably clear.

If the citizens of Fort Worth and Dallas will forgive me for discussing them in the same paragraph, the entire area is growing so rapidly that many man-made hazards now interfere with safe flying operations.

CORPUS CHRISTI, TEXAS

Corpus Christi International

The approaches are flat, and pilots like them.

However, there are many thunderstorms and showers, and the winds are erratic. Therefore it is not always possible to use the "long" runway (5600 feet), which is adequate for small jets. Landing on the short runway under adverse weather conditions is marginal, and sometimes becomes critical.

HUNTSVILLE, ALABAMA

Madison County Airport

This small community has become important as a space program center; many of the scientists commute between Huntsville and Cape Kennedy. Since they are familiar with the air and its hazards, they must close their eyes and pray every time they fly out or in. Their airport has the dubious distinction of being one of the most notoriously unsafe in the United States. It has a black book of hazards.

Let me take a deep breath and begin. There are severe (to put it mildly) obstruction problems. The Cumberland plateau scenery is lovely, with the town's public square standing on a bluff seven hundred fifty feet above sea level, but bluffs don't help pilots.

Only three miles from the runway there is an obstruction 890 feet above sea level. At two miles, there is one 770 feet above sea level. *Both* are directly on the center line of the approach path to the instrument landing runway.

There is an obstruction of 1061 feet only one mile east of the approach end of runway number eighteen. There is another of 1570 feet only two miles to the southwest.

At the far end of runway number eighteen there is a pit, or quarry. In the event of an aborted take-off on eighteen an airplane might very easily plunge two hundred feet into it.

There are high tension lines on one side.

The Redstone Arsenal is only one and one-half miles from the runways.

No, Huntsville is not popular with pilots ... (Interestingly, the FAA has authorized a new airport for Huntsville. The location is *one mile* from the wild-life refuge of millions of ducks and geese. Beware the birds!)

CINCINNATI, OHIO

Greater Cincinnati Airport

This airport is strictly a one-runway operation, north-south. It has an ILS system, and the associated lighting systems are adequate. But the runway is marginal in length at 8600 feet. A second runway is only 5499 feet long, has no aids whatever, and is completely inadequate for medium-range and long-range jets. Piston airplanes and small jets may take off and land safely on this runway, provided, of course, that the weather is good.

This was the scene of a fatal American Airlines 727 accident, about which I'll say more later.

Back in the old DC-3 days, the Cincinnati airport, called

"Sunken Lunken," was built in a hollow that was frequently fogged in, and had a hazardous approach. The new airport is located across the Ohio River, in Kentucky, and another runway is under construction. There is a terrain problem: the hills are rugged. And there are downdraft winds that make the airport only marginally safe for jet airplane operations. The "Sunken Lunken" days are gone, but weather and terrain problems remain.

COLUMBUS, OHIO

Port Columbus International

The Columbus airport has a runway 10,700 feet long. As a matter of fact, Columbus has two jet runways. So far, all to the good. But wait.

The two runways have been built in the same direction! And in Columbus, crosswind landings are frequently a problem. And, sorry to say, there is an obstruction on the approach end of the instrument landing runway. Because of this obstruction, the glide slope component of the instrument landing system is a steep one. Therefore the touch-down point is approximately sixteen hundred feet from the approach end of the runway. So for all practical purposes this runway is 9100 feet in length rather than 10,700 feet.

CLEVELAND, OHIO

Cleveland-Hopkins International

A city of this size and importance should have better airport facilities. The present airport is marginally adequate, but in no way outstanding. It has five runways; one of them, 9,000 feet, is fair for long-range jet use. Three of the others are usable by some jets.

Radio and instrument approach facilities are not bad, but Cleveland is topped by many cities that are smaller.

Sóme high tension wires run straight across the approach end of the instrument landing runway, number five.

The city is paying the inevitable price of growth and progress: commercial buildings, factories and towers are mushrooming, and these obstructions increase the airport's hazards.

This is a city that gets an "A" rating in any pilot's book.

DETROIT, MICHIGAN

Detroit has two major airports, both of them excellent. *Wayne County Airport* is used for long-run, international flights, and *Willow Run Airport* for shorter flights. In general, all facilities are very good, including approach and radio facilities.

Keep in mind that Detroit is a starting and terminal point for a number of regularly scheduled transatlantic flights. *Wayne County Airport* has one fine runway that is 10,500 feet in length. If I have any criticism at all of Detroit, it is that this is the only runway that can be used for long-haul operations.

INDIANAPOLIS, INDIANA

Indianapolis International

A splendid example of a modern airport. The instrument approach runway to the north is 10,004 feet. The associated lighting systems are good, but there are no touch-down zone or center line lighting systems.

The back course to the southwest has approach lights, sequence flashers and the visual glide slope. The northwest-southeast runway also has a full ILS system, but its length, 7604 feet, is marginal for jet operations. The taxi ways and high-speed turn-offs are adequate and well lighted.

The instrument approach runway is relatively free of obstructions, and a pilot doesn't have to hold his breath when he lands in Indianapolis.

LOUISVILLE, KENTUCKY

Standiford Field
There are three runways, only one of which is suitable for jets, and it is marginal, its length being 7800 feet. The 5000-foot east-west runway is being lengthened, but just to 7200 feet—still marginal.

The lighting systems are adequate. The airport is operated by the city, and the Federal Aviation Agency has frowned on the approach lights to runway number twenty-nine, but improvements have not as yet been made.

PHILADELPHIA, PENNSYLVANIA

Philadelphia International
A major international airport, with transatlantic flights originating and terminating here. Let me emphasize that even though the one runway may be a good one (none too good, at 9491 feet,) with a full ILS and good associated lighting facilities, such an airport is necessarily a *limited* one. When wind and weather do not permit use of the single runway, the airport is "out of business" for jet use.

It is often used as an alternate, when it may be legal but, in the opinion of pilots, questionable.

The other runways are completely inadequate for jet operations. Runway number twenty-seven has the back course of the ILS, but is equipped with *no* other aids.

I'm none too happy about the one jet runway, since there are many obstructions on the approach path.

PITTSBURGH, PENNSYLVANIA

Greater Pittsburgh
This airport is far better than Philadelphia's. It has two paral-

lel east-west runways, each equipped with a complete ILS system and associated lighting systems.

The west approach runway is only 8000 feet in length, which is marginal for jet operations, but at the time of the present writing, it is being lengthened. Pittsburgh takes pride in her airport, and is quick to make improvements when they are needed.

ST. LOUIS, MISSOURI

Lambert Field

This airport cannot be characterized as either "good" or "bad." It has features of both. One of the worst enemies of take-offs and landings here is the weather: there are variable winds, high, strong, and dust-laden.

This airport is one of the oldest in the Midwest, and was built in the open country. But civilization has crept up on it, and it is now almost completely surrounded by private houses and other buildings. In fact, the approach to runway number twenty-four lies almost directly over an elementary school!

The main instrument approach runway is to the southwest, and is equipped with a full ILS and associated lighting systems. But at 7600 feet it is only marginal in length for jet use.

The long runway, which runs southeast-northwest, has a partial ILS system which provides the pilot only with runway alignment information. It has no equipment to give him glide slope or descent information. It has approach lights to the southeast, but no other aids to the northwest.

This runway is 10,018 feet in length, which would be good under normal conditions. Unfortunately, there is a considerable downward slope at *each* end. This, obviously, makes it difficult to land in the touch-down zone, and tends to shorten the effective runway length. (Note: the touch-down zone is usually an area between five hundred feet to fifteen hundred feet from the approach end; the ideal is one thousand feet. If a pilot touches down shorter than five hundred feet, he would be crossing the threshold at so low an altitude that he would be flirting with the potential disaster of an under-shoot, especialy on a marginal runway. If the runway is slick, the pilot must touch down as near the approach end as possible. Let me add that the difference between touching down at five hundred feet or fifteen hundred feet is only that of a clock's tick at the approach speeds of the modern jet airplane).

WICHITA, KANSAS

Wichita Airport

Scheduled airline traffic is relatively light, but there is considerable light airplane traffic here. The location of the airport is perfect: it is situated on flat plains, which provide an unobstructed approach from any direction. However, there are only two runways, one of them northwest-southeast, and the other north-south. The use of the latter is limited because of the strong winds that blow across the Kansas plains.

Both runways are marginal in length; the main instrument runway is 7300 feet long, the other 6300 feet. The instrument approach is to the north, and has a complete ILS system, with approach lights, sequence flasher lights, and so on. Approaches from any other direction are completely lacking in aids, however; there is no glide slope, and no runway end identification lighting system.

TULSA, OKLAHOMA

Tulsa International

A first-rate airport that is a pleasure for pilots to use, and one that ably serves the city.

It has complete ILS systems to the north and to the south. The longest runway is 10,000 feet; then there are an east-west runway of 7100 feet, and a southeast-northwest runway of 6360 feet. The last two would ordinarily be considered marginal for jet operations, and I do wish they were longer. However, circumstances alter cases, and strong headwinds, which are fairly constant, do a great deal to make up for the lack of runway lengths.

There are also two shorter runways which are used exclusively by light airplanes. This solves a major traffic problem, relieving congestion on the principal runways.

OKLAHOMA CITY, OKLAHOMA

Will Rogers World Airport
Another one-runway operation for jets, for all practical purposes. It is 9800 feet in length, north-south, has a complete ILS system to the north and a visual glide slope to the south. So far, so good. But winds are strong and variable in this part of the country, and crosswinds can make a landing on the one runway difficult. This is particularly true in the winter, when rain frequently freezes, and in the spring, when rains may be heavy.

There are two other runways, northeast-southwest, and southeast-northwest. The longer of them is only 5652 feet, so they are unsuitable for most jets, although they do relieve the principal runway of much light airplane traffic. A new north-south runway of 7200 feet is also in operation for light aircraft.

ALBUQUERQUE, NEW MEXICO

Albuquerque-Sunport
This airport (along with those in Phoenix and Tucson, Arizona, and Las Vegas, Nevada) is often called a "fair weather" airport. This bright and sunny description will not impress the pilot who has been caught in dust or rain storms—or even an occasional snowstorm.

Of these four airports, only that at Albuquerque has an ILS system. It is to the north, with associated approach and sequence flasher lighting systems. This aid is essential, for the land falls off abruptly on the west to the basin of the Rio Grande River, a nasty drop of some hundreds of feet.

This means that on an approach from the west, the pilot flies unaided over terrain that makes depth perception difficult. Wind currents can be tricky, and sudden updrafts and downdrafts are common.

The main runway at Albuquerque is 12,769 feet in length, quite adequate for the jets which normally fly in and out. The land rises rapidly to the east, however, and within twenty miles of the airport, just slightly north of due east, lies Sandia Peak, which is 10,695 feet high—a considerable obstacle. (In 1955, Sandia Peak figured in a controversial crash. Eventually, the CAB made one of its rare changes in determination of probable cause—from "pilot error" to "cause unknown.")

TUCSON, ARIZONA

Tucson International

This airport has no instrument approach system, much less lights of any kind except plain, old-fashioned runway lights. But there are redeeming features. The main runway, southeast-northwest, was planned with intelligence, and lies parallel to the valley in which the airport is located. This, alone, saves a pilot many headaches. Also, this runway is a good 12,000 feet long.

There are mountains to the east and to the west, but they lie at a considerable distance from the airport, and the actual approaches are made over relatively flat terrain. There is a 6000 foot long northeast-southwest runway which can be used if headwinds are strong.

PHOENIX, ARIZONA

Sky Harbor

Strictly a one-runway operation for jets. The main east-west runway is 10,300 feet in length, but lacks an adequate instrument approach system. There is a visual glide slope to the east, but there are no approach lights, no runway identification lights or any other approach aids.

145

This airport has a parallel east-west runway of 6000 feet, which is used by light airplanes. Traffic on it is considerable.

LAS VEGAS, NEVADA

McCarran Airport
When the weather is fair, which it is the better part of the time, this airport causes no major problems. But dust storms and occasional rain (once in a long while, snow, too) are nuisances. Winds may be tricky, and high temperatures create problems on take-offs. (When temperature rises, jet engine power deteriorates). So pilots using this airport on long-range flights sometimes encounter difficulties, particularly when taking off with crosswinds blowing.

The airport is located in a valley, cupped in on three sides by very rugged terrain. The east-west runway is one of the longest in the United States (12,545 feet), and compensates for many of the airport's deficiencies. There is also a north-south runway of 7503 feet, marginal for jet operations.

MIAMI, FLORIDA

Miami International Airport
In the main, this is good. It is almost completely surrounded by private residences and other buildings, but the terrain is flat, and all of the approaches are unobstructed.

The weather is the worst enemy of this airport, if the Miami Chamber of Commerce will forgive my bluntness. During the hurricane season winds may be fierce, and the city gets its full share of thunderstorms in the spring and summer.

The airport is adequately equipped with full ILS systems to the east and west on separate, parallel runways. One is 10,500 feet and the other 9349 feet. There is also a southeast-northwest runway, 8040 feet, with a visual glide slope to the southeast. There is a fourth runway, too, north-south, 6081 feet, which is

146

marginal for the larger jets except in strong headwinds. High winds can make up for lack of concrete, and a pilot prefers this combination to strong crosswinds on a longer runway.

ATLANTA, GEORGIA

Atlanta Airport
First of all, Atlanta has a wide range of approaches. The land is relatively flat; there are a few small hills to the west and north, but all of them less than one hundred feet high, so for all practical purposes the approaches are unobstructed from all directions.

There are two parallel east-west runways, each with a complete ILS and associated lighting systems to the east. (However the parallel runways, though recently installed, are too close to permit simultaneous IFR approaches.) Also, to the west, are the back courses of the ILS, which give a pilot runway alignment information. Both west approaches have visual glide slopes, and are very good. The runways are of adequate length for jets with medium-range fuel requirments.

To the northwest is another excellent approach, with an adequate runway. There is also a northeast-southwest runway of 6937 feet, with no approach aids.

The Atlanta Airport handles a considerable volume of traffic, so, in spite of the good approaches and runways, there are frequent delays on both take-off and landing. Here we see a pattern that repeats itself in many American cities. Atlanta's equipment is good, but growing traffic is the villain. Like so many others, this airport is falling behind in the struggle to keep pace with the increasing traffic.

BALTIMORE, MARYLAND

Friendship International
This serves Washington, D.C. as well as Baltimore itself. It is

infinitely superior to National Airport, but is not in a class with Dulles. The instrument approach is to the east, with a complete ILS system, high intensity approach lights and strobe flashers. However, there are no center line or touch-down zone lights. This runway is 9450 feet in length, is of black-top construction and is well marked. The approach to the west is also acceptable, with ILS for runway alignment, and visual glide slope.

Friendship Airport's other runways score lower. There is a southeast-northwest runway of 8400 feet, which is adequate for long-range jets, but to the northwest it has no approach aids. A southwest-northeast runway is only 6000 feet in length, which is marginal for the big jets. There are no approach aids, but it does have runway end identification lights.

Obstructions do not create serious problems.

This airport is something of an "ace-in-the-hole." It is used as an alternate airport for landings on many occasions when weather on the eastern seaboard of the United States is bad, and New York, Boston and Philadelphia are closed in, although Chesapeake Bay doesn't escape its own share of fog.

CHARLESTON, SOUTH CAROLINA

Charleston AFB/Municipal

A first-rate airport, with virtually all of the facilities needed by jets. It has two jet runways, the longer of them 9000 feet, and both usable. Its approach systems are excellent.

This airport is used jointly by the city and the United States Air Force, and it is axiomatic that whenever the Air Force moves in, equipment is uniformly good, up-to-the-minute and not permitted to deteriorate.

HARTFORD, CONN.

Bradley Field

Bradley, located at Windsor Locks, also serves Hartford's

148

neighbor, Springfield, Massachusetts. Hartford, "the insurance capital of the country," apparently doesn't practice what it preaches. There are fine homes, department stores, shops and restaurants in the city, which indicate citizens of substance. Bradley Field doesn't reflect this substance.

Runways are marginal, as are approach systems. There are some obstructions, although the airport *is* located far enough from the center of the city to reduce these hazards. On balance, there are many airports in the United States that are superior to Bradley Field, but there are others far worse.

SAN FRANCISCO, CALIFORNIA

San Francisco International

Emphatically not the favorite of pilots!

Non-stop transoceanic flights originate and terminate in San Francisco, which means a very long haul, indeed. Consequently the big jets must be heavily loaded. And San Francisco's renowned climate and geographical beauty are no help to the men who fly jets.

As every sport fan knows, the winds that whip through the Giants' Candlestick Park do strange things to a baseball sailing through the air. They also blast at airplanes with great authority, generally from the west.

There are four runways, two of them east-west, and two north-south. Three of them are more than 9500 feet in length, marginally adequate for large jets; however, because of the heavy loads these aircraft must carry, I would be happier if the runways were still longer. One north-south runway is 7005 feet in length, marginal.

The airport is located on San Francisco Bay, with a mountain ridge between the field and the Pacific Ocean. On a clear day, passengers enjoy a spectacular view. In bad weather, however, pilots really have their work cut out for them. In general, overrun or clear-way areas, where an airplane can, if necessary, finish its landing roll-out in relative safety, are clean extensions, often graded, sometimes partly paved.

When taking off to the west, an airplane literally climbs between two mountain peaks, and a heavily loaded jet flies through the gap at an altitude lower than that of the crests of these peaks. Strong winds often roar through the mountains, and turbulence can be considerable. It is always possible that an airplane just taking off might not have attained sufficient speed to penetrate this turbulence and stay controllable. Also, when taking off on this course during bad weather or at night, a pilot must be exceptionally careful to hold his ship on a very straight course. A failure of directional indicators could create a critical situation.

There are compensations, to be sure, since San Francisco is as thoroughly modern and advanced a city as can be found in the United States. The instrument approach, which is to the west, is equipped with the best of up-to-date equipment, including a full ILS system, approach light and flasher systems. To the south there are a visual glide slope, approach lights and sequence flashers.

The approaches to the west and to the south are over the Bay, and hence are unobstructed. Circling approaches to the north or east are difficult. There is a take-off over the bay which is also unobstructed—but in case of an aborted take-off, a heavily loaded jet would undoubtedly end up in the water.

LOS ANGELES, CALIFORNIA

Los Angeles International

This is the largest and busiest airport on the West Coast, and although I hate to be caught in the middle of the rivalry between Los Angeles and San Francisco, this is the better airport.

Pilots agree that the airway traffic control system here is more efficient than that found at most airports, and this, alone, does a great deal to reduce problems.

Unfortunately, the approach end of runway number twenty-five lies directly over Inglewood and Watts, both very heavily populated, so there are noise abatement problems. Pilots are directed to fly as high as possible on their approaches; also, because of noise abatement programs, airplanes seldom take off toward the northeast.

For years Los Angeles was noted for its smog, and the airport had its full share. Recently, however, the campaign being waged by the entire community has begun to show dramatic results: smog is already much reduced, and there is every reason to believe it will continue to diminish.

There is an on-shore breeze, which means that the majority of operations are conducted toward the west, in the direction of the Pacific Ocean. Consequently there are three east-west runways. Another, north-south, is used only when there are high winds. It has no approach aids.

Two of the runways are pilots' favorites. They are 12,000 feet in length, and are equipped with full ILS and associated lighting systems. The third runway, east-west, is 8925 feet—longer than the jet runways at many other airports, used here mainly by piston and light airplanes. It has no approach aids.

Los Angeles has long been renowned for the eccentricity of some of her citizens, and a handful of the more eccentric have created a new hazard. Irate because of the noise made by jet airplanes, they have actually been known to fire at aircraft that roar over their homes. Fortunately for everyone concerned, they are poor shots.

SAN DIEGO, CALIFORNIA

San Diego International—Lindbergh Field
A pilot who is a close friend of mine was discussing the San

151

Diego'airport recently, and said, "I think this place is the most horrible example of a jet airport in the United States. I'm willing to bet there are more tires blown trying to get an airplane stopped on that runway than anywhere else."

This is the one jet runway, east-west. It is 8700 feet in length, more or less marginal. At the eastern end a pilot must run an obstacle course, clearing both a ridge and a United States Navy hospital. A turning approach and steep descent are necessary in landing.

Only two miles from the airport is a 1000 foot "crossing altitude restriction," that is, a requirement for noise abatement procedures.

The instrument landing facilities are poor. In fact, the approach is too steep for a glide slope to be effectively useful.

"And take-offs," my friend adds bitterly, "require an immediate, sharp right turn to reduce the noise over the homes of retired Navy admirals."

SEATTLE-TACOMA, WASHINGTON

Seattle-Tacoma International

This airport is located adjacent to a plant where Boeing builds jet airplanes. The company, naturally, has its own airport, and pilots for scheduled commercial carriers are warned not to become confused and land at the wrong one.

The airport is built on the razor-back of a ridge, which requires a pilot to handle his aircraft with great care in adverse weather. There is a complete ILS system, and one good jet runway, east-west.

PORTLAND, OREGON

Portland International

A good airport.

There are two jet runways, with a complete ILS on the longer.

The terrain is flat, and there are few obstacles.

All is not roses at Portland, however. The airport itself is built on sharply elevated land, close to the water, and, as a consequence, may be closed in very quickly by fog and other bad weather conditions.

MINNEAPOLIS-ST. PAUL, MINNESOTA

Minneapolis-St. Paul International Airport
One of the most efficient in the country. Tower traffic control is crisp and alert. Facilities are modern, and are kept in good condition.

There are two jet runways, each equipped with complete ILS and associated lighting systems. The longer of the runways is almost 10,000 feet in length, and has a "cushion" of an additional 900 foot overrun.

I can think of only one hazard of any consequence. There is an automobile freeway to the south of the airport that is sometimes mistaken for a runway.

MILWAUKEE, WISCONSIN

General Mitchell Airport
Score—fairly good. It has two jet runways, and its other facilities are adequate, but it is cursed with obstacles, some of them unusual. There are four strange looking man-made obstacles known as "jet blast pads," one located at each end of each jet runway. These concrete mounds, each one hundred feet high, deflect the blast of a jet's engines upward in order to prevent automobiles from being blown off the adjacent roads. This, of course, is splendid for motorists, but creates hazards for pilots.

A lakeside airport (Lake Michigan), the field is subject to fogs and low ceilings. This hazard is complicated by the presence of a formidable obstacle on the instrument landing approach path, an AC Sparkplug tower. The control tower is alert to its dangers,

153

and not only does the pilot use his own aids to clear it, but ground radar is also used, with the controller advising, "You have now passed the tower, and are clear to land."

NEW ORLEANS, LOUISIANA

International-Moisant Field
Facilities, including runways and lighting systems, are, in general, adequate, but there is a dangerous obstacle that pilots dread. A high ledge has been built to prevent mud from oozing onto the runways; this ledge creates as many problems as it cures. There are no overruns in the stopway areas—just the ledge, so a pilot must keep in mind that if he lands a little short, his landing gear will "trip"; and if he lands too long, he may find himself in the mud of Lake Pontchartrain!

SARASOTA, FLORIDA

Bradenton Airport
There are three runways, two of them suitable for use by medium-range jets, but facilities are only fair. There are no high intensity runway or approach lights. Neon advertising signs are everywhere, though.

Pilots must approach runway number four across a highway, with many obstructions, including telephone and electric lines, and buildings, including the Circus Hall of Fame.

Lead-in lights are sadly lacking, with the result that when there is rain or fog it is difficult to find the very short runway number four.

PENSACOLA, FLORIDA

Pensacola Airport
Medium-range jets need all of the available runway to land, and the runway is in need of re-surfacing. This runway is partic-

ularly slippery when wet. Instrument landing facilities are limited.

ORLANDO, FLORIDA

Orlando Airport
A dream airport, with the best of all modern facilities.

There are two parallel north-south runways, each of 12,000 feet, each with an overrun of 1000 feet at each end.

Approaches are flat, and free of serious obstacles.

This field is also used by the United States Air Force (McCoy Base), which explains a great deal. At noted previously, when the military has joint use of a field, little, if anything, is lacking.

TAMPA, FLORIDA

Tampa International Airport
Worthy of its international name. Tower traffic control is efficient, and facilities are good. The runways are adequate for jets, and although parallel, are located sufficiently far apart to insure safety. There are complete ILS and associated lighting systems over the land approaches.

MONTGOMERY, ALABAMA

Dannelly Field
Only one jet runway, east-west, is adequate for jet use, but it is good, with a length of 9000 feet and an overrun of 1000 feet at each end. The surrounding countryside is flat, and there are no serious obstacles.

MOBILE, ALABAMA

Bates Field
This seaport field lies on flat ground, and approaches are over flat terrain. It is located on the Gulf of Mexico, however, so frequent fogs impede visibility. It has no other serious problems.

LEXINGTON-FRANKFORT, KENTUCKY

Blue Grass Field

This airport is located in rolling hill country that is an asset rather than a liability. The approaches are attractive, which the passengers enjoy when the weather is clear, and the approach paths are marked by easily distinguished horse farms.

There is only one jet runway, number four, which has complete ILS and associated lighting systems.

BIRMINGHAM, ALABAMA

Birmingham Airport

This airport combines the good and the bad.

The field itself is located in a basin, surrounded on three sides by high hills. When landing on runway number twenty-three it is necessary for a pilot to fly very close to the ridge top, and then follow the terrain closely down to the runway.

Runway number five has a prime approach which is excellent. Balancing this, however, is runway number eighteen, called by a close colleague of mine "impossible."

NORFOLK VIRGINIA

Norfolk Airport

I'd like to add a few specific words on the problems created by poor or shortsighted planning. The airport at Norfolk, Virginia illustrates my point all too precisely, I'm afraid.

This airport was built in the 1940's on the foundation of what had previously been a golf course. The beautiful, sandy loam of tidewater Virginia provides a substantial base that is easily drained. One would think it would be difficult, if not impossible, to make a mistake in airport planning.

The men who built the Norfolk airport, however, placed it between two lakes that are utilized in the city's water system. In all justice to the planners, of course, no one except aircraft designers with gleams in their eyes were thinking of jet airplanes and their highly specialized needs. But wherever the blame, the Norfolk Airport, adequate once for piston airplanes, has caused one soupy headache after another since the inception of the jet age.

The city now faces a virtually insoluble problem. It needs a modern jet airport, for progress and growth. Other land is now difficult to find and buy. But, in order to make the present airport suitable, it would be necessary to disrupt the city's whole water system, at great expense and equally great inconvenience.

Norfolk is not alone in its dilemma. The problem is one that the whole United States must solve for the sake of safety, and to assist the inevitable further expansion of jet airplane travel.

OMAHA, NEBRASKA

Eppley Airfield

Eppley is located on a large bend in the Missouri River. It has two runways. One is north-south, 6001 ft., only adequate for propellor and smaller jets. It has no associated approach aids except identification lights on the north end and the regular low intensity lights. The main runway is southeast-northwest, 8500 ft., with an ILS system to the southeast. This runway has approach lights and sequence flashers on both ends. The airport doesn't have a particularly heavy volume of traffic but serves a large area. Located on the river, it is surrounded on all sides by higher terrain and has a high percentage of fog and low ceiling. There are also a lot of gusty winds from the north-northwest in winter and south-southwest during the summer months.

LINCOLN, NEBRASKA

Lincoln Municipal/AFB

Thirty-five miles to the west-southwest of Lincoln is an old Air

Force' field. It has a north-south runway of 12,900 ft. and is on high flat terrain unobstructed from any direction except for the city itself to the east-southeast. It has a complete instrument landing system including approach lights and sequence flashers operating northward. Due to the location this airport is a better bad-weather airport than Omaha. However this entire area is subject to low ceiling due to the gradual western uptrend of the terrain toward the Rocky Mountains, and these low ceilings can prevail for extended periods of time under certain weather conditions.

DES MOINES, IOWA

Des Moines Airport
    This is a one-main-runway operation orientated southeast-northwest like the other airports in this area. (This, of course, is to accommodate for the prevailing winds. However, quite strong winds can blow from any direction across these plains.) This runway is 9000 feet and has a complete ILS system with approach lights an sequence flashers operating to the northwest. The terrain is relatively flat with only a few hills of 100 ft. or less to the north and east, so for all practical purposes it is an unobstructed approach. From the opposite direction, southeast, the runway has only end identification lights and no other approach aids. There are two other short runways, one 5,000 feet and the other 4,500 feet which are good for light plane traffic. This airport also has a heavy percentage of fog and low ceiling, especially during late fall, winter and spring months.

SIOUX CITY, IOWA

Sioux City Airport
    This is the same story as Des Moines except that like Omaha it is Missouri River bottom land. Again, it is an old Air Force field with three runways, giving the pilot a choice of six different landing directions, to suit the varying wind conditions. Although

158

the north-south runway is marginal in length all runways have a cleared overrun area of 1000 feet—a very definite plus. On the other hand, both in Kansas City, Missouri, and Sioux City, Iowa the runway ends have high dikes with the rivers beyond them.

RENO, NEVADA

Reno Airport

The airport, serving the resort area of northern Nevada, is located in a bowl with mountains on all sides. It has a 9000 ft. north-south runway with an ILS system to the south, also approach lights and sequence flashers. There is an east-west runway of 6105 feet with no approach aids except regular runway lights. Weather and wind are important factors, especially during the winter and early spring. The landing minima are 1000 foot ceiling and two mile visibility, so the pilots find that quite often they have to pass up Reno.

SALT LAKE CITY, UTAH

Municipal No. 1

The airport is just to the east of the Great Salt Lake and just to the west of a high ridge of the Rocky Mountains. This includes the Grand Tetons which is one of the most famous tourist attractions in the entire Rocky Mountain range. Such tourist attractions do not usually insure good flying and Salt Lake Airport comes in for its share of bad weather and winds. However, this is not a major factor and it certainly does have a favorable percentage of good weather.

It is a one-main-runway operation oriented north-south parallel to the mountain range to the east. The ILS is to the north and has approach lights, sequence flashers and all associated aids. To the south there is the back course of the ILS for runway alignment; that is, the pilot can tune in as for a north approach (0°) and his ILS needle will provide the same visual guide even though he is flying south (180°). To the south there is also a visual glide slope

159

for descent, but no approach lights. The approach lanes to both directions of the one runway are relatively unobstructed. However, due to the surrounding high terrain the initial approaches are higher and do require a higher than normal descent. Even the final approach requires a slightly higher than normal descent.

There are also a parallel north-south runway of 6710 feet and a shorter southeast-northwest runway. Neither has any approach aid. The main runway has 1700 feet of overrun area on the north end and 150 feet on the south which makes this a quite adequate runway as long as wind and weather conditions permit its use.

PORTLAND, MAINE

Municipal Airport

Years ago this was called the Stroudwater Airport. My home town (Cape Elizabeth) is nearby. Here I first soloed. (The plane was a Fleet biplane, license number 711V.) This was near the end of the helmet and goggle days, and some people were still saying that "If God intended man to fly, He would have given us wings."

I frequently see Portland Municipal Airport from thirty thousand feet, to and from Europe. It has been improved over the years. There are two runways, and it can accommodate medium or short-range jets. The facilities compare favorably with other airports serving similar size cities.

But (hoping that the Chamber of Commerce will forgive me) weather conditions have not changed over the years. Sea fogs and nor'easters create problems for pilots who fly in and out of the old Stroudwater Airport.

TORONTO, CANADA

International Airport

Located north of Lake Ontario, International Airport has

three runways suitable for jets. One can accommodate heavily loaded transatlantic flights.

Good facilities include two separate ILS systems. Problems include noise abatement regulations like the United States ones, with a system of preferential runways to "protect" adjacent residential areas. (Canadian authorities evidently are concerned about these regulations, and print the following on the pilots' noise abatement procedure charts: "Notwithstanding the foregoing procedures or any instructions relating thereto issued by air traffic control, decisions affecting the safe operation of the aircraft shall remain the captain's prerogative.")

MONTREAL, CANADA

International Airport
This is a busy international airport with three runways, as at Toronto, one of which is suitable for heavily loaded long-range jets.

Good facilities include three separate ILS systems. Problems include noise abatement regulations, the preferential runway system being used under certain wind and weather conditions.

Light airplanes operating out of nearby *Cartierville Airport* cause a traffic problem.

Pilots are perfectionists . . . for your sake. In "scoring" these major jet airports, we have thus rated them against the ideal, and criticized them where they fall short. You may want assurance that most of them are above the "average," but in the matter of safety the "average" is intolerable, and improvement is obligatory, however embarrassing, difficult, or costly.

I urgently hope that every reader of this book will join with the fraternity of airline pilots and become a perfectionist . . . for safety.

XI

THE FAIL-SAFE CREW CONCEPT

Many readers are familiar with the phrase, "fail-safe," if not with all its meaning. Basically, the fail-safe crew proponents believe that an airplane should be manned by sufficient competent personnel trained to fly and land an airplane safely in the event that the captain or co-pilot should become incapacitated by sudden illnesses, food poisoning, virus, etc.—or even die.

At the beginning of the jet age, pilots believed that all three members of the required cockpit crew should have the qualifications of a pilot. This concept touched off a bitter, continuing battle between the pilots and the airlines, between pilots and flight engineers, and even between carriers that have held opposing opinions. Jurisdictional disputes between unions erupted, issues became emotionally complicated and, eventually, distorted.

After all this hard feeling, time, training and expense, the safety battle was lost. It has been a costly one for most of the carriers and the pilots. It was also costly for some outspoken flight engineers—who lost their jobs. To date, no one has "won," *including the public.*

On long-range and most medium-range jets, there are three men in the cockpit, each with his specific duties and responsibilities. The original jets were designed to operate with a three man crew. The U.S. airlines have a wide range of qualification

163

requirements for the men in the third seat. Their basic qualifications range from aircraft and engine mechanics to commercial pilots with instrument ratings. Even among the "big four" carriers there is an extremely wide range of required qualifications. On one of these carriers, which I shall call Airline "A", all three crew members are pilot-qualified, and the co-pilot and pilot engineer often exchange seats on different legs of a flight, similar to a "musical chair" arrangement. Obviously, in the event of an emergency, such as the captain's becoming incapacitated, this is most desirable. Airline "D" has the opposite point of view. Its third crew member does not have *any* pilot rating. He cannot fly, or assist in the actual flying in the event of an emergency.

Airlines "B" and "C" have compromise fail-safe crew concepts. Their third crew members hold commercial pilot licenses and are given two or three landings in the jet for their original qualifications. They are not kept proficient, however, and most of the Airline "B" or "C" third crew members could not actually land a jet any more than Airline "D's" unrated man.

Now let's thicken the stew of confusion.

The industry has designed the short-range jets eliminating the third seat completely, and thus limiting the crew to two rather than three men. The new Douglas DC-9, the British-built BAC 111 and the new Boeing 737 are highly sophisticated pieces of equipment and are operated in practically the same manner as the heavier, longer-range jets.

The FAA should *not* have made this distinction in certifying these jets for two-man crews.

Is it safe to operate with a one-man crew?

I have known instances in which a pilot has become incapacitated or even died while his aircraft is in the air. Obviously, this can create a dangerous situation. It *has* happened that many lives have depended on the ability of one man to bring the flight to a safe landing.

The carriers have been going through a period of rapid expansion, hiring new co-pilots of relative inexperience; most are excellent men who will eventually develop into competent captains.

I myself know co-pilots whose flying I have observed and many of them could not, with their present training and experience, land a jet airplane safely, under all types of conditions, should the captain become incapacitated.

Let me emphasize that there are excellent pilots serving as co-pilots. However, their initial flight training hours in a new jet airplane are approximately one-half the time given to the more experienced captains. Eventually, they *do* acquire the necessary experience. However, the basic problem remains: a co-pilot should accumulate sufficient time *before* he serves as a crew member on a passenger flight.

Thus, in aircraft design, in specification of minimum crews, and training of new crew members, the FAA must finally face the significance of the fail-safe crew concept.

XII

HANGAR FLYING

Near-Misses

Here are a few typical incidents from my own experience.

On February 24th, 1963, I was flying from Kennedy Airport, New York, to Pittsburgh. I took off on runway number twenty-five, and in accordance with traffic control procedures, made an immediate left climbing turn to an altitude of two thousand five hundred feet.

While still in the climbing turn, I caught a glimpse, out of the corner of my eye, of another airplane on the same course, quite close to me. I immediately rolled sharply in a right diving turn to avoid a collision.

Subsequently I learned that the other aircraft was a Navy plane, headed for Floyd Bennett Airport, and that the pilot had not been in radio contact with the Kennedy control tower. Surprisingly, he was not required to get in touch with the tower, even though flying directly over Kennedy. Therefore no action was taken against the Navy pilot.

On December 2nd, 1965, I was flying from Cairo, Egypt, to Athens, Greece, over the usual airway route, at an altitude of 35,000 feet. On this flight an airplane passes through three control zones: the first is the responsibility of the Egyptians; the second is controlled by the Cypriots, from Nicosia; the third is the responsibility of the Greeks.

Well, another airplane had left Cyprus en route to North Africa, and our paths crossed. Both of us were flying at 35,000 feet, there were ice crystal conditions, and visibility was limited. While cruising I suddenly spotted the vapor trail (called the con-trail) of another airplane a very short distance ahead of me.

Literally an instant later I saw the other airplane, directly to my left. It disappeared, and I flew through its con-trail.

Normally, two airplanes crossing the same point have a time separation of at least fifteen minutes. In this situation, I estimate, we were ten seconds apart, twenty seconds at the most. Just thinking about it gives me a chill.

A subsequent investigation disclosed that the airplane in question was an RAF Canberra jet. But the pilot denied that he had been at the intersection point at the time I had indicated. No further action was taken.

I don't want the reader to think that I'm incident-prone, so here is a recent near-miss experienced by a fellow pilot. On September 11th, 1966, he was flying from Rome to Madrid at an altitude of 35,000 feet, and was still under Marseilles traffic control. Suddenly he saw another airliner, belonging to a foreign carrier, flying eastbound. The pilots could have waved to one another—if they hadn't been so busy avoiding a collision.

My friend heard the other pilot ask Barcelona control the American's altitude, and was told 35,000 feet. With some heat—and who can blame him—the foreign pilot told Barcelona that he, too, had been cleared at 35,000, until exactly sixty seconds earlier, when he had been told to descend to the 33,000 lane. He told Barcelona control he should have been cleared out of the 35,000-foot level sooner, which is putting it mildly.

Bomb Scares

No scares, I think, are worse than bomb scares.

On January 31st, 1960, I had just taken off from Kennedy (at that time called Idlewild) when I received an urgent radio message to the effect that someone had just called the airport, saying that a bomb had been placed on board my airplane.

I was given an immediate traffic clearance to land, and I can assure you I wasted no time putting my aircraft on the ground again, in as gentle a landing as any I've ever made. I taxied to the terminal at once and advised the passengers to leave the airplane without delay, telling them what had happened, and explaining that we were probably the victims of a "crank" call, but could take no chances.

I'm thankful that the end of the story is anti-climactic. We made a thorough search of the airplane, and found no bomb. Thank the Lord.

On December 26th, 1963, I was involved in an even more dramatic bomb scare. I had originated a flight in Los Angeles, and, eastbound to New York, had landed in Las Vegas. As I taxied out to the Las Vegas runway, one of the hostesses came forward to tell me she was having trouble with a drunken passenger, who was carrying his own bottle of liquor. I instructed her to take the bottle from him, telling him she was following the orders of the captain. She did, and the drunken passenger obeyed, but was annoyed, naturally.

I reached the end of the runway, completed my preflight check and taxied into take-off position and was clear to go.

Suddenly the control tower operator said, "Hold it! Don't go!"

I reduced my thrust to idle and stopped the initial roll.

After a few seconds, he said, "start taxiing back to the terminal building."

I started toward it, waiting for an explanation.

Then he came on again to tell me there had been a report of a bomb on board.

I immediately passed the information along to the passengers, as in the other case. I felt sorry for the passengers—including the actor Cary Grant. It was one o'clock in the morning, and everyone had been hoping to catch up on some sleep. In fact, Grant had told me, when we had been chatting prior to boarding the airplane, that he had planned an especially busy day in New York, and that he needed all the sleep he could get.

It was obvious to me that no one was going to get much sleep for a few hours.

When we reached the gate, I had the passengers deplane at once, leaving their hand luggage and other belongings behind. It was important that they leave the airplane as quickly as possible, in an orderly fashion.

There was no panic, and they started filing out.

At that point the hostess came forward to the cockpit again, and told me the drunk had said to her, "Don't worry, I've got the bomb."

I started back at once, threading my way through the line of passengers. The hostess pointed out the drunk to me, and I clamped a hand on his shoulder.

He muttered something, and tried to wrench free. I kept a firm grip, and escorted him—with some force—into the terminal building, where I handed him over to the police.

By this time the place was swarming with law enforcement officials, who had responded at once to the scare. City police were out in force, and so were deputy sheriffs. Several F.B.I. agents were there, too. (The sabotage of an airplane—or even the threat of sabotage—is a Federal offense.)

I learned that the sheriff's office had received a telephone call from a woman who said that her husband was taking my flight to New York, and was planning to kill himself with a bomb that would explode in mid-air. This call, of course, had triggered the alarm.

I told the sheriff's men about the drunk, who was taken off to an upstairs room for questioning.

Several officials and I returned to the airplane, where a search had already begun. The hostess, justifiably nervous, gave me the seat number where the drunk had been sitting. I stood on the

170

seat, and there, in the rear of the overhead rack, was a small package . . .

Taking a deep breath, I gently picked it up and handed it to the official in charge, Capt. Bell, who immediately removed it from the airplane.

Meanwhile the thorough search of the aircraft continued.

The package, a rapid investigation showed, was nothing more than a harmless gift that the drunk was apparently taking to someone in New York.

In the meantime the F.B.I. had succeeded in tracking down the husband of the woman who had made the telephone call, and he, too, was taken upstairs for questioning. Other officials raced out to the woman's house.

The questioning lasted for some time. Before it was completed, the men searching the airplane established to their satisfaction, and mine, that there was *no* bomb on board the ship.

The questioning dragged on, and it became evident that the drunk knew nothing about the supposed bomb. He had been angry because his bottle of liquor had been taken from him, and his comment to the hostess had been a smart-alecky crack.

All the same, he was in serious trouble, and was placed under arrest. Federal, county and local governments do not take kindly to threats of airplane sabotage.

The woman who had made the telephone call to the sheriff's office finally confessed the truth. She and her husband had been quarreling, and he had left her. To make trouble for him, she had invented the whole story!

What she succeded in doing was to make a great deal of trouble for herself. She, too, was placed under arrest, and charges were brought against her.

By this time it was after 4:00 a.m. There had been a delay of more than three hours, and everyone, passengers and crew members alike, was wide awake. We boarded the airplane again, and the flight proceeded without further incident.

The hostesses told me that the passengers remained awake for the rest of the flight to New York. (I've wondered, occasionally, how Cary Grant got through his difficult day's schedule.)

I wasn't bothered this time at being more than three hours behind schedule because the bomb scare had proved a hoax.

But I trust these stories do point up the need, mentioned earlier in these pages, for stricter controls to reduce the hazards of sabotage.

Since 1955 there have been five known cases of aircraft sabotage:

On November 1st, 1955, a bomb exploded on a United Airlines DC-6, over Longmont, Colorado, on a flight from New York to Seattle. Forty-four passengers and all crew members were killed. It was subsequently proved that a man had taken out a life insurance policy of $37,500 on his mother, who was a passenger on the flight, naming himself as beneficiary. He was executed for the crime.

On July 25th, 1957, near Daget, California, dynamite exploded in the lavatory of a Western Airlines Convair while the ship was cruising at 10,000 feet. The passenger who set off the charge was killed, and a large hole was blown in the fuselage. The pilot displayed exceptional skill, however, and managed to land his ship safely. There were no other casualties.

On January 6th, 1960, dynamite exploded on board a National Airlines DC-6 flying from New York to Miami, the blast occurring near Bolivia, North Carolina. All twenty-nine passengers and five crew members were killed.

On May 22nd, 1962, near Unionville, Missouri, there was an explosion in the lavatory of a Continental Airlines Boeing 707, while the ship was cruising at 39,000 feet, en route from Chicago to Los Angeles. The aircraft crashed at the Iowa-Missouri border, killing all thirty-seven passengers and eight crew members. It was later determined that the bomb had been placed in the lavatory by a passenger who had taken out a large sum of insurance immediately prior to the flight.

On May 7th, 1964, near San Ramon, California, a Pacific Air-lines Fairchild turboprop (jet engines *with* propellers) crashed, out of control, after the Captain and his first officer had been shot by a crazed passenger. Forty-one passengers and three crew members were killed.

Inasmuch as the insane are always among us, more effective controls should be established immediately to reduce the threat of sabotage.

A Common Passenger Query:
"How safe is flying with one engine out, two engines out, three engines out—or even four engines out?"

Don't get the wrong idea about the modern jet airplane. It is a marvelous flying machine.

The reader has already seen that a serious situation arises if one engine should fail on a heavily loaded airplane at the critical point of take-off. In an engine failure under other circumstances, however, the passenger has no need for worry. Once the modern jet airliner is in the air, it can continue to fly with ease. I'll admit I wouldn't be too happy if an engine should fail over the middle of an ocean, with a long way still to go to reach an airport, but I wouldn't necessarily be too much concerned, either. If a second engine should fail, and there is a suitable airport within a reasonable distance, the pilot would be able to execute a landing safely.

A jet can remain in the air for a surprisingly long time with only one engine operating. It would not, however, be able to maintain its altitude for very long, and would be forced gradually to descend. The pilot would be faced with a number of problems, but in all likelihood would not find them insurmountable. Depending upon the weather, the weight of the airplane and other conditions, he could travel a reasonable distance and make his landing.

Obviously, if all four engines fail, the plane starts to descend immediately. It becomes a mammoth glider, with a rate of descent approximately three or four thousand feet per minute.

If a jet engine actually flies apart—a rarity—the turbine pieces may be hurled into the adjoining engine and damage it so that it, too, would fail.

The control problem becomes aggravated when an engine, particularly an outboard engine, fails. This creates a powerful leverage and power pull on one side, with less on the other. Two engines failing on the same side accentuate the problem considerably. In the take-off of a heavily loaded airplane, the directional control would be critical. Once airborne, however, and flying at a higher speed, the ship becomes much easier to handle, and although I wouldn't say there is no control problem, it should not be critical.

I want to say a final word about engine failure on take-off. As I have said earlier, the failure of one jet engine need not be serious, unless complicated by other problems. The failure of two jet engines on take-off is something else. If such an event occurs, around or over the V-1 decision speed, an accident is almost inevitable.

Breaking Regulations

My hangar flying stories wouldn't be complete without the recounting of at least one occasion when I was forced to fly "illegally" in order to fly in the safest manner.

There is an endless flow of rules from the paper mills of the government and the air carriers. I have often thought that a pilot should have a law degree before applying for employment with the airlines. This endless flow of rules forces pilots into a conflict: fly legally but less safe, or violate the rules and fly safer.

One incident occurred a few years ago, on a flight to Washington, D.C. from New York. The wind was blowing at forty miles per hour as I came down at the National Airport, which created a special problem: I had lost the use of one of my four engines on the flight.

The only runway on which I was *legally* permitted to land was the north-south runway, but the wind was blowing from west to east, which would have meant coming down into a very strong crosswind on three engines, a hazardous operation.

174

I elected to land on a shorter runway that was not approved, but would take me directly into the wind. This was by far the safest course I could follow, since the wind would substantially reduce my landing speed. In this way there was no danger of overrunning or overshooting this short runway.

Well, I *did* land safely, without incident.

We pilots who fly the Atlantic frequently fly illegally because a situation demands it for safety's sake. I'm referring specifically to an approach to a storm area, when the cell of the storm is directly on the airplane's route.

Now, a pilot must obtain clearance to deviate from his route. But, in mid-Atlantic, communications with the controls either in North America or Europe are frequently delayed. So a jet traveling at approximately six hundred miles per hour could find itself in the center of a very dangerous cell before the pilot could obtain clearance to deviate from his course.

Naturally, we use our "emergency authority," and deviate from the course.

I might add that this same situation arises occasionally on flights over the continental United States, but is becoming increasingly rare on domestic flights. Communications within the country have shown a vast improvement in the past few years, and only very infrequently does a pilot encounter a communications lag that requires him to use his "emergency authority" to deviate from a course in order to avoid a storm cell. In this field, air-to-ground and ground-to-air technology has kept pace with the swift development of aircraft design.

As for illegal deviations on transatlantic flights, they will continue. The pilots, whose primary concern is safety, have no intention of changing their habits or casting aside their better judgment for the sake of legality. It is the procedures that will have to be changed.

As a pilot who is a close friend of mine said recently, "I prefer to break regulations—which I consider synthetic in the first place—rather than break the structural limits of the aircraft I'm flying."

XIII

THE GOVERNMENT'S ROLE IN AVIATION

How the Camel Got Its Nose Into the Tent

In 1918 the U. S. Post Office Department inaugurated airmail service between Washington, D. C., and New York City. Three Army pilots took off from Haines Point, which was later made famous when the veterans marched on Washington and General Douglas MacArthur and General Eisenhower drove them off with cavalry. Two of the airplanes finally made it; the third picked up the shorelines of Chesapeake Bay, attempted to follow it, and became somewhat disoriented—the pilot eventually crashed while attempting to land near Norfolk, Virginia.

The government has been an active participant in commercial aviation since 1926 when the Bureau of Air Commerce came into being. It seems normal enough that commercial aviation—a fledgling enterprise which was to grow into the best system of transportation in the world—should have been supported and nursed along by the government. Obviously no one business interest could have mustered the necessary financing for the proper development. From 1926 through 1938 the government's role was fundamentally that of a passive participant. The airway beacon lights were installed and the old Adcock radio ranges gave out their series of A and N signals which, when merged, formed a steady hum to let the pilot know that he was "on the beam." There was a certain amount of airport construction know-how parceled out by the tenderfoot bureaucrats and occasionally some person with a small gold badge and title of "inspector" would show up around the airport and jam his thumb through a fabric covered wing, in a rather unscientific attempt to test the airworthiness of a plane.

After the Federal Aviation Act of 1938, however, the government's role started to expand. In the heyday of Franklin Roosevelt, the old pilot-civilian training program was born and placed under the jurisdiction of the fledgling Civil Aeronautics Administration. The demand for small aircraft training increased. Additional personnel were hired and stationed at the manufacturing plants. The airway traffic control system, started earlier by a corporation formed by the airlines, came into being. The federal government began to take over the operation of control towers, previously a function of the airport management. World War II was on the horizon and pork-barrel politicians with an eye to the future made sure that some military training bases were so located that they could be utilized as the municipal airports of the future.

The Civilian Pilot Training Program was probably one of the best run government programs ever. Also, the airport construction program was good for its day and time. During the war years with the major part of the U. S. civilian air transport fleet engaged in military operation, the Civil Aeronautics Administration played a relatively small role, with the major portion of the country's resources going towards the military's effort for a successful end of World War II.

Since 1946, the worm has turned again. The corps of approximately ten thousand employees of the CAA at the end of World War II has grown to more than forty-five thousand employees of the FAA!

Sheer numbers do not guarantee efficiency. All too many pilots feel that the FAA has degenerated into a bureaucracy which often engages in the face-saving of its public image rather than the pursuit of air safety.

178

THE GOVERNMENT'S ROLE IN AVIATION

The Federal Aviation Agency is charged by the Act of 1958 (a not too studious rewrite of the act of 1938) with that prime responsibility—air safety. This includes the certification of aircraft and airmen for the protection of the public. Whenever there is an accident or an "incident" affecting safety, the FAA is as responsible as anyone; for if there is an error in design, manufacture, maintenance or operation, their obligation towards public safety has been involved.

But a review of accident findings would open a serious question about how well this obligation works. Pilots are the fall guys, and "Pilot Error" has become a nauseating phrase to me and my colleagues. I submit that if aviation is to grow on a safe and sound basis, we must now lessen the government's influence.

The government's role must change from intimidation and self-justification to support. *To this end, I recommend that the FAA staff of flight inspectors be reduced.* The responsibility for training programs, flight instruction in new types of aircraft, and assurance of proficiency should be vested entirely in the management of the airlines involved. Every carrier in the United States can then be expected to perform with the highest degree of responsibility, instead of walking with a government crutch (wanted or unwanted).

Second, the airway traffic control system, one of the largest FAA divisions, must be totally changed. There is just not enough time at modern high speeds to have the aircraft separation function performed strictly by a human controller on the ground. Long ago the green-yellow-red light superseded the traffic officer on the corner—and it is high time we modernize in the air as well. Qualified private enterprise can do a better and more businesslike job of effecting air traffic separation.

Third, in the airworthiness of aircraft, the government's role must be lessened. They say that "A camel is a horse built by a committee"—and so is a manufactured machine supervised by bureaucrats. The inspector corps must be substantially reduced in number, and those who are assigned at aircraft plants must be better qualified and more responsible to the public.

179

The Procedure Syndrome

Procedures in themselves are not evil. What happens all too often, however, is that a happy improvisation by crew members is "plagiarized," subtly changed . . . and then given back to those same crew members as law. Here is how it happens.

When an airline agrees to specify the procedure in its operating manuals, the procedure may become incorporated into the FAR—Federal Air Regulations—which have the force of law in every conceivable matter from the minimum number of cabin attendants to the speed by which a command pilot must decide to take-off or abort.

It is the inflexibility of these government regulations that is the bane of every crew member's existence.

To go back over the years, these procedures were originally conceived for two purposes: to aid a pilot and the members of his crew in the performance of their many chores when flying from one city to another, and to perform these tasks with the greatest measure of safety attainable.

Through the years, however, accidents have occurred; there have been investigations, law suits, blame-fixing, face-saving, and the consequent inevitable piling up of regulations that accumulate when dealing with a bureaucratic arm of government. The result is something of a muddle, and some mandatory regulations are actually dangerous to follow.

A story—a true story, unhappily—will illustrate how some procedures come into being. When jets were first introduced into commercial aviation in 1959, the pilots refused to fly them until the airlines agreed to a contract. The hammering out of the agreement took time, and one airline asked their supervisory personnel to operate a few flights.

Some of these men, former pilots, had been sitting behind desks for years, and had forgotten much of what they had known, but they went off to school again, and were, in time, approved by both the airline and the FAA to serve as operating crew members on jet airplanes.

180

During one flight, the captain went back to the passenger compartment for a chat with some friends, leaving the co-pilot in charge, with the airplane actually being flown under the control of the automatic pilot.

Well, the autopilot disengaged, and the airplane began to descend. The desk-ridden co-pilot must have lost his sensitivity to change, and did not feel the drop. And as it fell, the airplane gathered speed rapidly. (I might explain that a jet is not like a conventional airplane which has a natural tendency to return to level flight; a jet tends to descend ever more steeply as it increases speed.)

The pilot returned to his seat, and by the time he had pulled out of the dive, the plane had lost thirty-one thousand feet! And the high-speed pullout bent the airplane, causing considerable structural damage.

As a result of such incidents, the FAA issued a regulation requiring pilots to remain at their stations throughout a flight. A good regulation? Emphatically not![1]

The pilot of a huge jet must bear his responsibilities and also stay alert for emergencies. He should relax for short periods, particularly on long flights. He needs to stimulate his circulation and relax his nerves.

Common sense would indicate that after such a short break the pilot will be far better able to perfect his approach and landing, as well as cope with any mechanical malfunction or emergency.

The FAA and Air Safety

Regardless of my own feelings on the subject, which are rather strong, I believe that in the interests of objectivity I should refrain from commenting at too great length on the role of the United States Government in the promulgation and maintenance

---

[1] During the period Captain Lowell was writing this book, the new Administrator of the Federal Aviation Agency, General McKee (who comes from a family of physicians) relaxed the rule.

of air safety. I would be remiss, however, if I failed to indicate what I consider glaring inconsistencies in the positions taken by the government agencies in dealing with matters of air safety Thus I ask you to scrutinize the following quotes from the *Policy Statement of the Federal Aviation Agency,* published in April, 1965.

On pp. 19-20, when discussing a policy of safety for safety's sake the FAA states: "The difficulty with the *mythical objective* is that it cannot stand without a serious implicit qualification—namely, 'the highest level possible within the framework of an economicaly viable and efficient air transportation system.' The consequence is an inconsistency between the objective and the implementing policy of safety for safety's sake. *It is simply not possible to pursue safety for safety's sake in an effort to achieve the highest level of safety without being seriously limited by the compromises necessary in the interest of a reasonably costed, efficient and viable system.*" (Italics mine).

But there must be no sacrifice of safety because of "reasonable costs", "efficiency", or a "viable system." The flying public is entitled to the highest level of safety it is possible to achieve!

Again, on p. 21, the same booklet states: "... it must be recognized that the probability of an aircraft accident in scheduled air carrier operations is now very low. *This means that any single step taken to improve safety in scheduled air carrier operations will have, in most instances, a small or possibly negligible effect when considering total operations. Therefore, any safety improvement involving a relatively substantial cost to the Agency or to the system should hold promise of a relatively substantial effect. It then follows that, because the Agency's resources are limited and the effect of most individual safety improvements will be small in any case, the Agency must devote its resources to identifying and implementing those improvements which will have the greatest effect relative to cost.* This approach to safety is not intended to ignore the cumulative effect of small gains which are possible at small cost; it would only require that each proposed gain promise an effect commensurate with cost." (Italics mine).

THE GOVERNMENT'S ROLE IN AVIATION

I find it incredible that safety improvements must be measured according to a yardstick of cost. I hold the unalterable opinion that *the only yardstick must be the saving of human lives!*

Let's turn now to another government-published document, *Policy Planning for Aeronautical Research and Development*, a Staff Report prepared for the use of the Committee on Aeronautical and Space Sciences, United States Senate, printed on May 19th, 1966.

On p. 93, it states: " ... the amount of money spent by the government for aircraft safety research is very small both in terms of total dollars and in relative effort compared to other aeronautical research and development." (As a matter of fact, the Staff Report reveals that *a mere 10% of the money* goes for studies and tests of devices or techniques intended to improve the operational safety of aviation. The lion's share is actually a subsidy to manufacturers, concerned with such development as increasing the passenger capacity of aircraft!)

Significantly, on the same page, it says: "Present research indicates that fatality and injury rates per aircraft accident can be decreased. Improvements in seat design, survival equipment, and procedures for evacuation can slow loss of life where the accident is potentially survivable."

This states precisely what we pilots have long maintained!

On the bottom of p. 93, this same document declares: "The airlines have active programs to provide the air traveler with dependable and safe air transportation. For instance, a new flame detection and suppression device has been recently developed which will virtually eliminate the possibility of lightning igniting volatile fuel vapors vented from fuel tanks."

I'm delighted that such a device has been developed. But I would like to ask a question: *Why aren't the airlines required by FAA regulation to install this device?*

One of the most telling observations to be found in this staff report appears on p. 91: *"All things considered, however, aviation safety cannot be said to be on a truly improving trend."*

The record clearly indicates that the Staff Report is, unfortunately, correct. It indicates that the FAA, in the fulfillment of its primary mission, *safety*, has failed. Passengers and crews continue to lose their lives unnecessarily.

XIV

THE 727 STORY

The story of today's air safety would not be complete without discussing the situation of the Boeing 727. This airplane was involved in a series of accidents after it had been in commercial operation for several months. Perhaps no pilot can be completely objective about an airplane that he has flown and which has been faithful to him. Jets are very complicated machines. The intricate procedures followed must be rigidly adhered to in order to achieve the full potential value of the jet's performance. A manufacturer may occasionally offer an exaggerated claim of an aircraft's performance, for sales purposes. I, for one, have never seen an airplane that completely lived up to its early specifications. Ordinarily, practical experience shows that they cruise a little slower, take a little bit longer to get off, and in general, fail to live up to that certification process we had discussed previously. Not much, but just enough, to become troublesome on occasion.

The Boeing 727 was hailed as a plush service airplane for smaller airports and new route segments not previously offered jet transportation. This airplane is not used on the North Atlantic routes that I fly, but as thoroughly as possible, I have investigated its performance characteristics. There are many things the reader should know.

The "T-Tailed Tigress" Is Born

As the industry progressed and "jet set" living became th
atmosphere most young people dreamed of, it appeared logica
and possible to offer the advantages of jet transportation t
smaller communities. Since weight is fundamentally the limitin
factor in getting aircraft in and out of short runways, if smalle
cities with shorter airports were to get the "jet set" treatment i
was obvious that a new aircraft would have to be introduced.

British manufacturers were already engaged in building
smaller jet transport called the Trident—it incorporated innova
tions not previously used on jet airline transports. The thre
engines were mounted on the rear of the fuselage and the hori
zontal stabilizer was at the top of the vertical fin—hence the terr
"T-Tail." U.S. manufacturers followed the design trend as in th
automotive field the Corvair followed the Volkswagen. There ar
things to be said for the "cleanliness" in design of th
fuselage-mounted engines, since obviously there would be les
drag from the air. There are other things, however, which mus
be considered, such as the basic law of physics which made ear
lier designers prefer the wing-mounted engines. Overly simpli
fied this related to the stall characteristics of the aircraft: th
airplane's front end was heavier, so when it stalled the nose drop
ped. When the nose dropped, gravity and aerodynamics com
bined to make speed build up. When speed built up the plane wa
out of the stall and again controllable.

The aft-mounted engines changed things somewhat. Here w
have a predominantly tail-heavy aircraft, and if the tail drop
first, gravity pull is the same but aerodynamics are reversed an
we are not controllable again so quickly. The aircraft starts t
descend still in a stall.

Another thing about the aft-mounted engine. These are just a
thirsty as those which are wing-mounted. The main reservoir fo
the tons of fuel is the wing cells. The only way to feed th
engines is through a tube leading back either above, below o
alongside the passenger compartment. This tube is as big as you

arm. You can imagine the results if this breaks and fire starts.
(This fuel line did break in the Salt Lake City accident. It may
have been the greatest single tragic contributor to the deaths
here.)

I must say that no single aircraft design ever had more public
appeal than did the Boeing 727. The FAA gave it airworthiness
certification. Every carrier that could get it, bought it. (Eastern
Airlines dubbed it the "Whisper Jet".) Pilots who had not experienced some of its "Delilah" qualities loved it, and passengers
stepped on one another's toes getting aboard. For several months
nothing happened. Then, in quick succession, came four tragedies.

Two of these aircraft crashed into deep water. The first one was
in Lake Michigan; the authorities have not completed investigation of this accident at the time of this writing. The last one was
in Tokyo Bay; the chairman of the team investigating that one
has told the Japanese Diet that evidence points towards pilot error
in a failure to arrest a rapid descent during the nighttime approach to Tokyo International Airport. However, the other two—
one which crashed on approach to Cincinnati, Ohio Airport and
the other which crashed making an approach to Salt Lake City,
Utah Airport—have been investigated and determinations of the
probable cause have been made. In both cases, the results have
been called *pilot error*. (In the other two cases, which crashed
into water, strong inference has been made that these, too, were
pilot error.)

I have some strong views concerning these 727 accidents.
These views are in disagreement with the CAB reports, but I
intend to get at the truth.

The Salt Lake City Accident

On November 11th, 1965, a United Airlines Boeing 727, in a
flight that had initiated in New York, with a stop in Denver,
crashed as it came down for a landing at the Salt Lake City airport. Out of a total of eighty-four passengers and six crew mem-

bers, there were forty-three people killed. Among the survivors was the pilot, Captain Gale C. Kehmeier, a veteran of twenty-five years with United, who had logged almost eighteen thousand hours of flying time.

Captain Kehmeier is the only surviving command pilot of the four crashes. Feeling it would be important to obtain his story for inclusion in these pages, I tried to get in touch with him. After some difficulty I found him living in Denver, Colorado. We corresponded, and held several telephone conversations. Finally, on October 2nd, 1966, I flew to Denver from New York to confer with him, and was an overnight guest in his home.

Before letting Captain Kehmeier tell his own story, I'd like to fill in the reader on the background of his situation. The Civil Aeronautics Board, (in what may well be record time) in its official report on the accident, adopted June 23rd, 1966, said the probable cause of the accident was "pilot error."

The only live pilot of four similar crashes, and the Civil Aeronautics Board did not believe his story! Instead they built a case of a poor pilot training record which Captain Kehmeier's own airline disputed.

On p. 24 of the official report, the CAB said, "The training record of this Captain indicated a pattern of below average judgment as well as a tendency to deviate from the standard operating procedures and practices. Indeed, it is significant that this case history not only reflects an apparent indifference in adhering to acceptable procedures and tolerances in general, but specifically during the landing or ILS approach phases of flight."

This statement is a direct contradiction of United Airlines' own report, dated April 8th, 1966, and signed by E. O. Fennell, Senior Vice President of United Airlines. On p. 8, par. C, "Pilot Proficiency as a Factor," he states:

"The impression created by the use in the Flight Crew Training Section of the Operations Facts Report (Ex.2-A,P.S.) of every instructor and check pilot comment made with respect to below average performances throughout a twenty-five year professional airman's career seems patently unfair to the air-

188

man, his employer, and the Federal Aviation Agency, which granted him the license to perform as a transport pilot. A review of any airman's file in the industry will indicate that below average performances are to be expected from time to time, especially during training and checking, and that instructors and check pilots are models of silence with respect to comments concerning average or better performances, and quick to comment concerning less than average performance in a certain area. The system would be valueless otherwise. But to isolate twenty-five years of such comments in four and a half pages of a summary report is, indeed, to create a biased and inaccurate impression. The below rewrite previously submitted prior to the hearing is drafted in a less biased manner more accurately to reflect the training history of the Captain."

The United Airlines report then summarizes Captain Kehmeier's training record, at the end of which it declares: "His last en route proficiency check was given on September 8th, 1965, and he was given an overall evaluation of above average."

In its final paragraph relative to training, the United Airlines' report states: "The conclusions fairly to be drawn from Captain Kehmeier's training and operational flying record is that his proficiency to fly the Boeing 727 aircraft as a pilot in command has been adequately demonstrated to both the Federal Aviation Agency and to United Airlines. To distort this record after an unfortunate accident—to make it appear that it gives some indication that he lacked proficiency—does not serve the goal of aviation safety."

The CAB report deals at some length with Captain Kehmeier's failure to pass his original "check out" test, which would have enabled him to fly the DC-8, a jet airplane. He returned to schedule flying on the DC-6, a propeller airplane. Later he passed check-out tests qualifying him as a command pilot for the Boeing 720 (a smaller version of the 707), and later, still other tests qualifying him as a command pilot for the 727. In neither of these examinations did he encounter any difficulty of any kind.

I would like to interject a comment of my own here. When a

pilot first switches from propeller airplanes to jets, it is not uncommon for him to fail these proficiency checks. It has happened to many pilots on every airline. There are *many* pilots flying jet airliners today who failed to qualify the first time they took their flight tests making the transition to jets. I agree with Mr. Fennell of United: Captain Kehmeier was "made to look bad," when what actually happened was routine.

I have myself studied and analyzed Captain Kehmeier's training as reflected by the CAB accident report and also his record as reflected by UAL. A word here about my own credentials as an analyst: I have given about 2,000 hours of flight instruction in many different airplanes, plus thousands of hours of on-line instruction to co-pilots. I have been a ground school and Link (flight simulator) Trainer instructor also. In my opinion, Captain Kehmeier has a record of which he has every right to be proud. It is above average.

Let me quote now from a report on these accidents made to the Air Line Pilots Association on March 29th, 1966 by Donald C. McBain, Central Safety Chairman, United Airlines Master Executive Council. On p. 4 he states: "My great concern in this matter is, as I have stated, the very strange coincidence of four 727 accidents in a short period and the fact that they have much in common. To find the pilot guilty in each case would be almost beyond the realm of possibility—in the only case where we have a surviving crew it would certainly appear that some members of the CAB staff are determined to build a case which will arrive at that conclusion. To find the pilot guilty unquestionably whitewashes all other parties, such as the engine manufacturer, the airplane manufacturer, the licensing agency, and even the carrier. But in the face of the facts involved in these four accidents, is the public interest actually served by distorting the records, by arriving at a probable cause which has been steered to clear all parties but one, and which—if wrong—will almost certainly cover up some flaw in the aircraft or its operations which will cause us another fatal, tragic accident?"

I now make public one of the most telling documents ever composed in the era of modern aviation—a personal letter from Captain Gale C. Kehmeier.

As the only surviving pilot of four Boeing 727 accidents occurring under similar circumstances, I must speak for four men. After the accident of Nov. 11, 1965, at Salt Lake City I gave my deposition from a hospital bed. At the Public Hearing in Salt Lake City on Feb. 21, 1966, I again told what had happened. Judging from the Aircraft Accident Report issued by the Civil Aeronautics Board on June 7, 1966, *they did not listen to me.*

The flight from Denver to Salt Lake City was normal, cruising at 33,000 feet. Sixty miles east of Salt Lake I was cleared to descend. On leaving ten thousand feet I cancelled Instrument Flight Rule clearance and continued descent with thrust levers fully retarded. About a mile out and a thousand feet above the ground I added thrust. I did not hear or feel any response and knew that I was in trouble. A landing was made short of the runway. By the time the aircraft skidded to a stop the cockpit was filled with smoke, and a fire developed with a resultant loss of 43 lives.

In the Public Hearing at Salt Lake City I feel that it was unfair not to hear all testimony and consider it in the findings. For example, the report distorts the level of my competency. My flight manager, Captain M. W. Wiley, and my Boeing 727 instructor, Captain Richard Boland, were present at the Public Hearing. They were not permitted to testify. Investigators for the CAB spent days interviewing co-pilots who had flown with me; the results of these interviews must have been favorable to me because they were never published.

Over a 25-year period, any airman will have an occasional below-average performance. Early in 1961, my DC-8 training was terminated and I returned to DC-6 flying. On May 5, 1962, I was given an en route proficiency check and received an "above average" rating in all areas. During the summer of 1963 I checked out in the Boeing 720 without difficulty. On January 2, 1964, I received an unsatisfactory grade in one maneuver in the aircraft portion of a Boeing 720 check. On January 4, I had a recheck and received average in all maneuvers except one, which was above average. Early in 1965 I progressed normally through Boeing 727 school and on Feb. 5 took a rating ride. Of the 64 items graded on the check ride, I received average on 51 and above average on 13. On May 3, 1965, while taking off in a Boeing 727, Number 3 engine caught fire. Check Pilot M. W. Wiley stated in his report: "No. 3 fire warning at rotation on 227-5 at Salt Lake. Emergency procedure and two-engine approach and landing properly handled." My last en route proficiency check was given on September 8, 1965, and I received an overall evaluation of above average.

As a further example of the unfairness of the CAB report, it notes on page 14, "There was no evidence of fire." The operations group report indicates that there were ten witnesses who observed fire prior to impact. This could account for no power prior to landing, particularly if the cables leading from the fuel controllers on the aft-mounted engines to the cockpit levers were subjected to excessive heat. At the Public Hearing I requested that three of these witnesses be allowed to testify. My request was denied.

Another example of how unfair the CAB was in the investigation was a graph produced from the read-out of the flight recorder. A note says: "Altitude Scale is ¼ horizontal scale." The result is distorted, showing abnormally steep glide. I have been informed since publication of the report that a revised profile takes into account lag in altitude instrument. Were the revised profile drawn to scale horizontally and vertically, with the altimeter lag taken into account, the result would concur with my testimony.

The Air Line Pilots Association conducted a survey which indicated that 24% of the pilots flying turbojet aircraft had experienced the phenomenon of slow spool-up of the jet engine. This information was vigorously objected to, and the ALPA was unable to get the results of this survey before the public.

Late in March I had two meetings with company officials. I was advised: "You will never fly again for United." I was given two tough choices: sign a resignation effective April 1, 1966, and receive $45,000 plus my lifetime pension . . . or be fired. Had I elected the latter course, Mr. George Foy, UAL attorney, indicated that the Federal Aviation Agency, through Mr. Ned Zartman, Regional Counsel in Los Angeles, was prepared to invoke an emergency suspension of my Airline Transport Pilot Certificate. After consultation with my attorney, Mr. Howard Erickson, and verifying the FAA's position via telephone, I decided to resign. After the resignation was signed, my attorney called Mr. Zartman and negotiated surrender of my ATR for a Commercial certificate with All-Type Ratings intact.

The tragic story of a man who was railroaded and used as a scapegoat.

The Cincinnati Accident
The CAB accident report of the American Airlines Boeing 727 crash at Greater Cincinnati Airport was released on October 7th, 1966. This accident occurred on November 8th, 1965 three days before the 727 crash in Salt Lake City. The CAB issued this Cincinnati crash report in approximately eleven months, which is about the norm. (They issued the Salt Lake City accident report, which occurred later, *before* the Cincinnati report, and in a record time of less than seven months. The CAB labeled the cause of the Cincinnati 727 accident as "pilot error". This fatal accident claimed the lives of 62 people including the pilots.)

On the first page of the report, the CAB states the probable cause. "The Board determines that the probable cause of this accident was the failure of the crew to properly monitor the altimeters during a visual approach into deteriorating visibility conditions."

In analyzing the CAB's report, I find this "probable cause" paragraph most objectionable. It is fabricated. No experienced pilot would have arrived at such a conclusion. As the story unfolds you will see why I make these statements. The first part of the report routinely deals with the history of the flight, including the control tower conversation with the pilot just before it crashed, weather conditions at the time of the accident, flight recorder readout analysis, etc.

Now page 24 of the report, Section 1.15 titled *Tests and Research*: "Examination of the AA 727 flight training curriculum disclosed that the normal Visual Flight Rules (training) pattern for Boeing 727 type aircraft (See Attachment #3) calls for the downwind leg to be flown at a distance of 1½ miles out from the runway. Since the flight recorder, ATC observations, and witness observed flightpaths all indicate that the downwind leg on this flight was flown at a distance of 4½ miles from runway 18, this aspect of the approach was explored in detail." The reader may note that the word "disclosed" implies that something was wrong, that the pilots deviated from an established training pattern. However, an American Airlines training and operations official explained this as normal, which it certainly was. We frequently must fly wide patterns for traffic separation and other purposes and I wondered why the CAB saw fit to insinuate that the pilots had done something wrong.

During the investigation, the CAB organized a Flight Control and Performance Characteristics Group. I would like to quote two paragraphs on page 30, Section 1.16. "This group was formed in light of another recent and generally similar Boeing 727 accident and following the suggestion that there might be some inherent design characteristic of the aircraft that might be in some way related to the cause of these accidents. This group was later expanded to encompass a subsequent Boeing 727 accident.

"The entire study disclosed no evidence of any design or performance deficiency and substantiated that the FAA and the Boeing Company had conducted extensive tests and research to validate and insure that the Boeing 727 complied with all applicable Federal Aviation regulations."

It doesn't state in this accident report exactly who participated in the study group. I do know, however, that representatives from Boeing Aircraft, who designed and built the 727, and the Federal Aviation Agency, who certificated the airplane as being airworthy, were the main participants. It is interesting to note that this group substantiated that the Boeing 727 complied with the FAA's own regulations. On the top of page 31, it states further, "Examination of the Boeing 727 technical data revealed that the two design features which serve to distinguish it from other jet transports were its three-engine configuration and sophisticated wing flap or high lift system. These unique features of the 727 design were explored thoroughly by the FAA during type certification and it was found that the performance and flight characteristics were in conformance with the design criteria and all applicable certification requirements." (Again the reader is reminded that FAA establishes certification requirements so one government agency, the CAB, in effect cleared another government agency, the FAA, of violating its own rules!)

"However, it was also determined that the high lift/drag ratio obtained in the 727 with full flaps extended requires the use of a comparatively higher percentage of thrust output than other models, in order to maintain desired landing speeds and rates of descent. At idle thrust and 40 degrees of flap the Boeing 727 descent flightpath at the minimum approach speed was about two degrees steeper than the average descent paths for the other models in the full flap landing configuration. It is recognized that the approach speed is lower for the B-727 than the other models with full flaps and idle power and that steeper descent paths in this configuration should, therefore, be expected."

Expected? Shouldn't they have said *avoided?*

On page 50 of the report they refer to the 40-degree flap position: "It should be stressed that because of the high drag characteristics of the aircraft in the 40-degree flap configuration, high descent rates and airspeed reduction, in response to decreased thrust, can develop more rapidly than in the less sophisticated models and that this flight regime should be avoided close to the ground. It was noted that most of the 727 operators have included in their flight manuals information concerning the avoidance of high descent rates during the landing approach and also, that the FAA has instituted a requirement for the demonstration of a low altitude high descent rate maneuver as part of the air carrier training programs." In changing the use of the flap setting the steep descent characteristics have been lessened and while the airplane may require a little more runway at high gross weight there is little doubt that safety is improved.

Most airlines have recommended against the use of the 40-degree flap configuration in the approach. My own airline has *blocked out this flap setting*. During the Civil Aeronautics Board hearing concerning the Salt Lake City accident, Mr. I. E. Sommermeyer, Vice President of Operations, stated that United Airlines had instructed their pilots to discontinue the use of the 40-degree flap setting and to use instead the 30-degree setting. Strangely, Mr. Sommermeyer referred to the instructions as "very routine." One participant observed that it was unfortunate that Mr. Sommermeyer hadn't issued these "routine" instructions a year or so earlier ...

A final factor in these accidents, and it has a direct relationship on the changed 40-degree flap setting, is the slow "spool-up" of the engines. Simply explained, this means an excessive delay in obtaining significant power when advancing from the idle range of the engines.

The United Airlines pilots who participated in the Salt Lake City accident investigation have stated it was a factor. Despite the fact that there are seventeen known cases of unusually slow spool-up of jet engines to date, the CAB discounts this possibility.

I note that the CAB, in several places in the accident report, praises the Boeing 727 flight performance in Madison Avenue language. *Why?* By a perversion of logic they used the airplane's excellent performance capabilities to indicate possible pilot

196

error. See page 50: "Also, consideration must be given to the fact that the 727 *does have* highly responsive and versatile flight characteristics and that these favorable characteristics may be misleading to the pilot, or are presenting the impression that greater liberties may be taken with the aircraft in normal operating situations, especially in the approach/landing regimes." I reject this insinuation.

On page 51, Section 2.2 titled *Conclusions*, the CAB sets forth in its initial statement in this section giving the airplane a 100% clean bill of health: "The entire investigation and in particular the specific examination of the Boeing 727 flight performance and characteristics revealed no design deficiencies or unsatisfactory operating characteristics. Furthermore, the latter review of the aircraft design aspects uncovered no factors that would have had a significant effect on the events leading up to this accident."

On page 52 of this accident report (*Conclusions*), the CAB must have had a powerful crystal ball or very strong ESP: "It is further concluded that after the flight turned onto the base leg in-flight visibility was sharply reduced and that both pilots became preoccupied in maintaining visual contact with the runway, resulting in inattention to, and improper monitoring of, the altitude reference instruments."

The deduction that these two dead Captains became "preoccupied" strikes me as a professional affront.

The CAB which had been pursuing the similarities of the four accidents suddenly does an about face on page 53: "While the circumstances and conditions of this accident are greatly different from those involved in another Boeing 727 accident which occurred at Salt Lake City, Utah, and for which the Board has already issued a report, there are some elements in common relative to pilot/crew judgment."

This paragraph insinuates to me that the Salt Lake City accident differs greatly from Cincinnati except for one common factor—the pilots used bad judgment. How do they know? The CAB didn't believe Captain Kehmeier's testimony under oath, and used their crystal ball on Captain Teelin and Captain O'Neill in concluding that they didn't monitor their altimeters.

In all of the 727 crashes, there has been one tragic similarity. Each occurred in the descent for landing.

In Cincinnati, the CAB concluded that the pilots didn't properly monitor their altimeters.

In Salt Lake City, the CAB concluded that Capt. Kehmeier failed to take timely action to arrest his descent.

Would an unbiased tribunal or a jury follow the lead of the CAB in exonerating the airplane manufacturer, the airline training procedures, and the Federal Aviation Agency who certificates the airplane and these procedures ... *and condemn the pilots*?

XV

AIRLINE SAFETY IS A MYTH

After all these revelations about various threats to airline safety, you are ready for a confrontation with the facts of life: *What is the state of airline safety today? Is it as safe as we are led to believe, or is airline safety a myth?* Be prepared for a few shocks . . .

Twenty-eight years ago, when I first started, flying was considered a hazardous occupation. This was backed up by insurance statistics. My life insurance rates were higher, back then, than the rates in most other occupations. In recent years, the government agencies, the airlines, the press and other news media have expounded on how safe flying is. At the same time, most public sources of information indicate that the automobile is a big killer. I decided to make my own comparison of these two modes of transportation and I researched each one.

The comparative unit for the U. S. official fatalities in the air and for automobile fatalities has been *miles*. Indeed, in comparing a machine whose average cruising speed is 500 miles per hour with a machine that averages around 50 miles per hour and using *miles* as the comparative, the airplane appears much safer. But now, let's look at the other side of the coin: Compare these two machines using a different unit of measurement, that is, *time*. This unit is the one that we mortals live in; seconds, minutes, hours, days, months and years.

AIRLINE SAFETY IS A MYTH

Using the time comparative, the unit of hours, for instance (which is the one that the mileage unit is tied to) and using the official fatality rates for a recent period of four years, we have a different story. *It is 30% more dangerous for a passenger in an airliner than in an automobile!* This fact was rather startling to me: one hour in an airliner 30% more dangerous than one hour in a car!

Here, for some years now, I have been telling my passengers at the end of the flight to be careful driving home, as the most dangerous part of your trip was about to start. Was I wrong?

Would you believe that on a time exposure basis a motor bus is twenty times safer than an airliner? That a train is thirty times safer than an airliner? It's true. *The time exposure ratio is* 1.3 *deaths in the air* (*scheduled airliners*) *for each one death in an automobile!*

On April 8th, 1966, *Time Magazine* published an editorial entitled "Safety in the Air," celebrating the eighth anniversary of the jet age. After pointing out that "flight has grown into an absolute essential for mobile, modern man," *Time* asks, "Is flying really safe?"

Answering its own question, the magazine replies, "It is. Scheduled airline flying in the U. S. is 6.4 times safer than personal driving; a person would have to travel 263 million miles in a plane, but only 41 million miles in a car, before he ran an odds-on chance of being killed. More people die by falling off ladders than by crashing in airliners. Life insurance is no more expensive for today's pilots than it is for bookkeepers; in a year, only one commercial pilot out of 1,000 dies in a plane. And the record is steadily improving; one accident occurred in every 85,000 hours of flight in 1959, but the rate in 1965 was one in every 800,000 hours."

Well, with all due respect to *Time*, flying is *not nearly* as safe as the editorial writer believes. The statistical base on which *Time*—and so many publicists for the aviation industry—rest their case, could be extremely misleading.

AIRLINE SAFETY IS A MYTH

Now, let's examine the fallacies in the record-keeping. When air fatalities are recorded, only *passenger* fatalities become statistics. *Crew fatalities are not included. Nor are non-revenue paying passengers* in some cases, that is, other employees of the airline who are "deadheading," or flown free of charge.

Also, tables of fatalities do not include fatalities caused by sabotage. In other words, accidents caused by bomb explosions in mid-air and other forms of sabotage are not shown in certain fatality rates. Yet, in 1962, for example, twenty-five percent of all deaths in the United States due to airline crashes were caused by sabotage. In 1964, this figure was thirty-seven percent. It immediately becomes apparent that the statistics on fatalities, as well as the base, are misleading.

It is a form of statistical sophistry to say that the individual citizen's chances of being killed in an airplane crash are one in each 263 million miles, while in an automobile they are one in every 41 million miles.

The very high speeds of the jet airplane, which eats up distance rapidly, make any statistics based on mileage misleading.

Suppose you are driving your car on a high-speed turnpike. There is no other traffic, you're on the road early in the morning and the weather is dry and clear. How much distance can you cover in one hour? Sixty miles? Seventy? Eighty, perhaps, if the state troopers don't nab you.

Now suppose you're traveling in a Boeing 707 or Douglas DC8 jet. How much distance will you cover in an hour? At a normal cruising speed, five hundred and eighty-five miles. More, if there's a tailwind.

My point is this: statistics on comparative safety should be put on a *time* rather than on a *mileage* basis. In other words, what are your chances of being killed if you spend one hundred hours in the air? What are your chances of being killed if you spend one hundred hours driving in your automobile? *The jet has made distance ratio comparisons meaningless.*

It seems to me that comparing the figures of automobile and

airplane fatalities according to the distance traveled is like setting up a comparison table for the automobile speed races at Indianapolis and a rugged motorcycle hill-climbing contest. Both of these sports are hazardous. Men who take part in either risk their lives, and are sometimes killed, sometimes injured. If mileage figures are used to compute fatalities, the racing car driver who whips around the track in Indianapolis will appear far safer than the motorcyclist who is bouncing and jogging up rocky hills.

Is he actually safer? Certainly not! He simply covers far more miles per hour. Hence any ratio using the number of miles traveled as its foundation gives a distorted picture of the actual risks taken.

I have no intention of frightening anyone. I earn my living flying an airplane, and travel many thousands of miles, spending many hours in the cockpit, every week of my life. I don't become nervous before flying, I don't lose sleep, and I certainly don't think I'm taking enormous risks. Neither do my employers, my cockpit and cabin crews, or the ground crews.

I do believe, however, that the time has come for the public to be given a more realistic picture of the actual situation, and I urge that future statistics be based on the time-exposure rather than the mileage basis.

The mileage yardstick delights everyone, including the government aviation agencies. It's good business. However, in dealing with the hard realities of air safety, the industry should not get trapped into accepting the statistical premise of the mileage criterion.

XVI

ACCIDENTS: PAST, PRESENT AND FUTURE

The first aviation accident in the U. S. which has been recorded was when one of the Coast Guardsmen assisting the Wright Brothers hung onto the wing too long and was lifted 25 or 30 feet in the air before dropping back to earth. He suffered a wrenched shoulder.

The first recorded aviation fatality occurred at Fort Myer when Orville Wright was giving instruction to Lt. Selfridge and Selfridge was killed. This accident was investigated by a military court.

Civil aviation was relatively unregulated until about 1926 when a small section of the Department of Commerce, which later became known as the Bureau of Air Commerce, established some ground rules for training, physical requirements, airplane maintenance, etc. As air transportation became more the mode and some public figures were involved in fatal accidents, the Congress enacted the Federal Aviation Act of 1938, establishing the Civil Aeronautics Authority. By administrative order and ostensibly to inject objectivity, the Civil Aeronautics Authority was divided into two sections, the Civil Aeronautics Board and Civil Aeronautics Administration.

The CAB's responsibility was primarily involved with the economic aspects of airline operation. It certificated air carriers;

and controlled route awards, ticketing costs, and related services. It regulated competition so that an orderly economic development of the air transport industry would take place. Its secondary but nevertheless very important responsibility was the investigation of and determination as to the probable cause of aircraft accidents.

The direction and control of the CAB was vested in a five-man board appointed by the President and approved by the Senate.

The Civil Aeronautics Administration was charged with supervision and certification of aircraft and component parts, flight crew members, air traffic controllers, mechanics, dispatchers and parachute riggers. They were also charged with enforcement of regulations promulgated by the board and if a person or corporation was cited in their enforcement procedures, his appeal from their efforts was to the Civil Aeronautics Board. The principal officer of the Civil Aeronautics Administration was an administrator appointed by the President and approved by the Senate. Later, by administrative order, the CAA was placed under the Department of Commerce and the CAB was attached to the Department of Commerce for housekeeping purposes. Pilots were never very favorably impressed with this system. Rightly or wrongly they had the impression that this was in fact an agency investigating itself.

When a series of mid-air collisions caused the Congress to take further action in 1958, we had great hopes. Many of us had pressed for a strong independent agency. Some of us thought we were getting it.

A careful comparison of the Congressional Act of 1958 and the Act of 1938 reveals a distinct similarity with the exception that the Civil Aeronautics Administration was removed from the Department of Commerce and set up under a new administrator. It was retitled Federal Aviation Agency and made responsible directly to the President of the United States. Now this administrator, to fulfill the broad responsibilities under this Act would have required wisdom and integrity far beyond the capabilities of most public servants.

He would be subjected to the pressures of one of the largest industries in the world. It would be most difficult, considering these pressures, to render objective decisions which were truly in the public interest. The average tenure of the administrators of FAA is something short of three years. As a matter of fact, we have had three administrators in just over eight years. It bears repeating that I believe the public will take steps required when supportable information is brought to their attention that a change is needed. I think one is needed now.

Back in 1926 very few people, except for a few old-time aviators, knew or cared about aviation. Since that time embedded bureaucrats have created a mystery about many facets of aviation. This has been a self-serving effort, I believe, to create the impression that certain expertise is needed to arrive at a determination of probable cause. It is ironic that Civil Aeronautics Board members have rarely had any real aviation experience in their backgrounds. They are only five in number, and they are vulnerable through their daily contacts with men who represent big company interests.

I have given considerable thought to the best way to decrease accidents. As a start, we must arrive at a correct probable cause for each accident. We must know the true reason so that steps can be taken to prevent a recurrence of the same circumstances.

The CAB pinpoints sixty percent of the probable causes as "Pilot Error." This label, along with "Acts of God" (bird strikes, sabotage, severe weather phenomena, etc.) maintains a nice public image for the industry and a favorable economic atmosphere for insurance claims. *However this label does not serve the public interest—air safety.*

How then *can* we arrive at the true probable cause? By *true adversary proceedings*. We need the nature of a courtroom, with two sides arguing the facts—a complete public airing. This can be accomplished very easily. These adversary proceedings can be conducted before a tribunal of judges, or a jury.

The preliminary phase of the present accident investigation system could remain, that is, the on-scene investigation and

205

fact-finding. The only recommended change up to this point is that all interested parties would participate on an equal basis: the pilot should be—and function as—not just an observer, but as an authority equal to that of the FAA, the manufacturers, and the airline.

The next phase would permit the facts brought out by the investigation to be subjected to arguments and cross-examinations and no group would be able to avoid the inevitable determination of the probable cause by a tribunal or jury.

Nobody, including the FAA itself, would have immunity. A study of the CAB reports will show that neither manufacturers, nor airlines—and certainly not the FAA itself—is ever clearly spelled out as the prime contributor to an accident's probable cause. (The reader can see for himself the consequences of partisanship and evasion of blame in the six years of accident report summaries that follow the main text of this book.)

Once an accurate determination is made, safety devices and procedures would of necessity follow in the definite direction of an improvement.

It is my hope that Congress will favorably consider legislation to make these procedures for improving accident investigations that I have outlined a reality.

CONCLUSION

In the preceding chapters I have tried to expose the shortcomings in many areas of airline flying, and to indicate remedial action that has become so urgently needed.

You will by now appreciate that flying is *not* safe enough . . . and it is *not* getting safer as the jet age progresses.

In years passed, I have taken action in many of these areas of my own profession, not only in my actual flying, but in the activities of appropriate groups who represent us, such as the Air Line Pilots Association.

My readers will now have an opportunity to join the crusade for air safety in some of the ways open. For some of the heroes of modern aviation must be ordinary citizens (including, I hope, some of you) who will press forward and inspire your own representatives to sponsor legislation that will enhance air safety . . . and save human lives.

A special note about the finality of the CAB determinations of "probable cause" of airline accidents. On February 14, 1967, another CAB determination was upset by the courts. In a unanimous decision, three judges of the U. S. Court of Appeals held that the government was also negligent in the 1962 crash of an Eastern Airlines DC-7 at Kennedy Airport for failure to provide the pilot with current weather conditions. This again highlights the need to eliminate biased CAB accident findings. *True* "probable causes" must be determined—corrective action must be taken to save lives.

APPENDIX
U.S. AIR CARRIER ACCIDENTS
(Key to Abbreviations)

Airline

AAA	Allegheny	NC	Northern Consolidated
AAL	American Airlines	NCA	North Central
AAT	Associated Air Transport, Inc.	NEA	Northeast
ACE	Alaska Coastal—Ellis Airlines	NOR	North Central
ACL	Alaska Coastal	NWA	Northwest
AFAX	American Flyers Airlines	NYA	New York Airways
ALA	Alaska Airlines	OVN	Overseas National
ALO	Aloha	OZA	Ozark
APA	Arctic-Pacific	PAC	Pacific
ARA	Argonaut Airways	PAI	Piedmont
AVA	Avalon Air Transport	PAWA	Pan American
AX	Aaxico, Inc.	PGA	Panagra
BAL	Bonanza	PNA	Pacific Northern
BLA	Blatz	PUR	Purdue Aeronautics
BNF	Braniff	PRE	President
CAL	Continental	RAA	Reeve Aleutian
CAP	Capital	RID	Riddle
CAR	Caribbean-Atlantic	SAS	Stewart Air Service
CBA	Caribair Airlines	SAT	Southern Air Transport
CEN	Central	SFA	San Francisco Airways
CHA	Chicago Helicopter Airways	SLIX	Slick
COA	Cordova	STA	Standard
COP	Capitol	SOA	San Francisco Oakland Airways
DAL	Delta	SOU	Southern Airways
EAL	Eastern	TRI	Trans International
ELL	Ellis Airlines	TTA	Trans Texas
FAL	Frontier	TWA	Trans World
FTLX	Flying Tiger	UAL	United
HAL	Hawaiian	USO	United States Overseas
IMP	Imperial	WAL	Western
KOAX	Kodiak Airways	WCA	West Coast
LAA	Los Angeles	WEA	Western Alaska
LCA	Lake Central	WLA	Wien Alaska
MOH	Mohawk	WOA	World Airways
MUN	Munz	ZATX	Zantop Air Transport
NAL	National		

Type of Service

C	Cargo	NR	Non-Revenue
CB	Company Business	NS	Non-Scheduled
CH	Charter	P	Passenger
D	Domestic	S	Scheduled
F	Ferry	T	Training
I	International	TF	Test Flight
MC	Military Contract		

Aircraft Manufacturer

A	Aeronca	DH	De Havilland
Aer	Aero-Commander	F	Fairchild
AF	Air Force	G	Grumman
AW	Argosy	L	Lockheed
AR	Armstrong-Whitworth	M	Martin
B	Boeing	PA	Piper
BAC	British Aircraft Corporation	Pil	Pilatus-Porter
Can	Canadair	S	Sikorsky
Car	Sud Aircraft's "Caravelle"	SN	Stinson
CV	Convair	V	Vertol
DC	Douglas	Vis	Vickers-Viscount's "Viscount"

Aircraft Damage

Dest.	Destroyed	Subst.	Substantial

Division of Injury

F	Fatal	S	Serious
M/N	Minor or None		

211

U.S. AIR CARRIER ACCIDENTS (ALL OPERATIONS) 1960

			Type of			Total	Passengers			Crew			Others		
Date	Location	Airline	Service	Airplane	Damage	Aboard	F	S	M/N	F	S	M/N	F	S	M/N
1/3/60	Philadelphia, Pa.	EAL	P, S, D	L-749	Subst.	51	0	0	46	0	0	5			
	Probable Cause: Fatigue failure of landing gear strut cylinder.														
1/4/60	Washington, D.C.	EAL	P, S, D	L-749	Subst.	65	0	0	60	0	0	5			
	Probable Cause: Fatigue failure of the right landing gear strut cylinder causing collapse of the right gear.														
1/5/60	Frankfort, Ill.	CHA	C, S, D	B-47G2	Subst.	1				0	0	1			
	Probable Cause: Failed to observe obstruction in flight path. Power plant malfunction due to fouled spark plugs.														
1/6/60	Bolivia, N.C.	NAL	P, S, D	DC-6B	Dest.	34	29	0	0	5	0	0			
	Probable Cause: The detonation of dynamite within the passenger cabin.														
1/13/60	Tampa, Fla.	DAL	C, S, D	C-46	Subst.	2				0	1	1			
	Probable Cause: The mixture control lever was rigged 5/16 inches aft of its proper position throughout its range, (idle cut off, auto lean and full rich). Very heavy layer of oil and grease on the starting ramp.														
1/18/60	Nr. Charles City, Va.	CAP	P, S, D	Vis	Dest.	50	46	0	0	4	0	0			
	Probable Cause: The delayed arming of the engine ice protection system while flying in icy conditions, resulting in the loss of engine power and attendant electrical energy required to unfeather propellers and relight sufficient engines to maintain flight.														
1/25/60	Boulder, Colo.	UAL	P, S, D	DC-7	None	26	0	1	20	0	0	5			
	Probable Cause: Turbulence in flight.														
2/4/60	New Orleans, La.	EAL	P, S, D	L-188A	Subst.	67	0	0	62	0	0	5			
	Probable Cause: The pilot failed to properly align the aircraft with the runway prior to landing in fog-restricted visibility.														
2/6/60	Chicago, Ill.	DAL	C, S, D	C-46	Subst.	2				0	0	2			
	Probable Cause: Unsafe landing conditions caused by ice on the runway.														
2/7/60	Los Angeles, Calif.	PAWA	P, S, I	B-707	Subst.	123	0	0	113	0	0	10			
	Probable Cause: Improperly executed ILS approach. Inadequate supervision by the captain.														
2/9/60	Tulsa, Okla.	CAL	P, S, D	Vis 812	Subst.	12	0	0	9	0	0	3			
	Probable Cause: Loss of directional control during landing in a gusty surface wind condition.														
2/13/60	Washington, D.C.	EAL	P, S, D	L-1049C	Subst.	38	0	0	33	0	0	5			
	Probable Cause: Failure of the exhaust manifold causing a fire warning necessitating an aborted take-off on a wet and slushy runway which afforded inadequate braking to stop the aircraft in the remaining distance.														
2/13/60	McGuire AFB, N.J.	AAT	P, MC	C-46	Subst.	57	0	0	54	0	0	3			
	Probable Cause: Crew failed to maintain an accurate log of the flight as pertains to flight planning/fuel consumption/fuel requirements.														
2/14/60	Providence, R.I.	USO	C, Public	DC-4	Subst.	2				0	0	2			
	Probable Cause: Failure to maintain sufficient altitude to clear obstruction during attempted VFR approach in IFR conditions.														
2/19/60	Utica, N.Y.	MOH	P, S, D	CV-440	Subst.	27	0	0	24	0	0	3			
	Probable Cause: Pilot lost directional control during landing in adverse weather and runway conditions. Questionable judgment of the pilot in using right reverse as the aircraft was sliding to the left and weathercocked to the right.														
2/22/60	Anchorage, Alaska	ALA	F	DC-6A	Subst.	4				0	0	4			
	Probable Cause: The pilot used improper power and flap settings resulting in an excessive rate of descent which was continued until the aircraft struck the ground.														
2/25/60	Chicago, Ill.	AAL	P, S, D	L-188	Subst.	27	0	0	22	0	0	5			
	Probable Cause: Accumulation of ice and snow on the runway. Darkness and reduced visibility, caused by snow showers.														
2/25/60	Chicago, Ill.	DAL	P, S, D	CV-440	Subst.	24	0	0	21	0	0	3			
	Probable Cause: Failure of the pilots to maintain sufficient airspeed during landing in a gusty surface wind resulting in an excessive rate of sink and hard landing. Lack of coordination between the first officer handling the flight controls and the captain handling the power controls.														

U.S. AIR CARRIER ACCIDENTS (ALL OPERATIONS) 1960

Date	Location	Airline	Type of Service	Airplane	Damage	Total Aboard	Passengers F	S	M/N	Crew F	S	M/N	Others F	S	M/N
2/26/60	Erie, Pa.	AAA	P, S, D	M-202	Subst.	16	0	0	13	0	0	3			
2/28/60	Olathe, Kan.	TWA	P, S, D	M-404	Subst.	9	0	0	6	0	0	3			
2/29/60	Chicago, Ill.	TWA	P, S, D	L-1049G	Subst.	63	0	0	56	0	0	7			
2/29/60	Syracuse, N.Y.	AAL	P, S, D	CV-240	Subst.	4	0	0	1	0	0	3			
3/5/60	Spokane, Wash.	NWA	P, S, D	DC-7	Subst.	70	0	0	65	0	0	5			
3/8/60	St. Louis, Mo.	EAL	P, S, D	DC-7B	Subst.	51	0	0	46	0	0	5			
3/9/60	Dominion Creek, Alaska	ALA	P, S, I	Cessna 180	Subst.	2	0	0	1	0	0	1			
3/9/60	Chicago, Ill.	AAL	P, S, D	L-188	Subst.	39	0	0	33	0	0	6			
3/9/60	New York, N.Y.	EAL	P, S, D	L-749	Subst.	23	0	0	20	0	0	3			
3/10/60	New York, N.Y.	AAL	P, S, D	L-188	Subst.	75	0	0	69	0	0	6			
3/16/60	Baltimore, Md.	AAL	P, S, D	DC-6	Subst.	25	0	0	20	0	0	5			
3/17/60	Nr. Cannelton, Ind.	NWA	P, S, D	L-188C	Dest.	63	57	0	0	6	0	0			
3/18/60	Lansing, Mich.	NWA	P, S, D	B-377	None.	67	0	1	60	0	0	6			
3/23/60	Mobile, Ala.	AX	C	C-46	Subst.	2				0	0	2			
3/24/60	Syracuse, N.Y.	AAL	P, S, D	DC-6B	Subst.	63	0	0	5	0	0	58			
3/29/60	Cape Pole, Alaska	ELL	P, S, D	G-21A	Dest.	3	0	0	2	0	0	1			
4/9/60	Fairbanks, Alaska	WLA	TF	F-27A	Subst.	2				0	0	2			

Probable Causes

- **2/26/60, Erie, Pa.** — Probable Cause: Failure of the copilot to establish and maintain alignment with the runway for take-off under instrument conditions. Failure of the captain to adequately supervise the take-off.
- **2/28/60, Olathe, Kan.** — Probable Cause: Fatigue failure left main gear gland nut. Contributing Factor: Rough surface of runway due to accumulation of snow and ice.
- **2/29/60, Chicago, Ill.** — Probable Cause: Fatigue failure of the right main landing gear drag strut.
- **2/29/60, Syracuse, N.Y.** — Probable Cause: Failure of the crew to ensure that the propeller blades were in reverse pitch before applying power for reversing. Malfunction of "B" circuit in propeller reverse relay control assembly.
- **3/5/60, Spokane, Wash.** — Probable Cause: Failure of the No. 10 connecting rod of the No. 4 engine. Prior damage to the No. 10 connecting rod by hydraulicking of the No. 10 piston.
- **3/8/60, St. Louis, Mo.** — Probable Cause: Loss of visual reference at touchdown, caused by obscuration of runway lights during hours of darkness. Improper supervision of runway lighting facilities.
- **3/9/60, Dominion Creek, Alaska** — Probable Cause: Failure to assure skis were fully extended and locked before landing.
- **3/9/60, Chicago, Ill.** — Probable Cause: Unwanted positive thrust on the right side at touchdown, caused by failure of the propeller control linkage disconnection on No. 4 engine. Patches of ice and snow on the runway.
- **3/9/60, New York, N.Y.** — Probable Cause: Material failure of the left drag shock strut piston shaft.
- **3/10/60, New York, N.Y.** — Probable Cause: Failure to provide adequate clearance from snowbank during turn onto taxiway. Taxiway lights obscured by snow at intersection.
- **3/16/60, Baltimore, Md.** — Probable Cause: The landing gear lever was inadvertently actuated above the *neutral* position before weight of the aircraft was firmly on the main landing gear.
- **3/17/60, Nr. Cannelton, Ind.** — Probable Cause: In-flight separation of the right wing because of flutter induced by oscillation of the outboard nacelles. Contributing Factors: Reduced stiffness of the structure; Entry of the aircraft into an area of severe clear air turbulence.
- **3/18/60, Lansing, Mich.** — Probable Cause: An evasive maneuver to avoid an imminent collision.
- **3/23/60, Mobile, Ala.** — Probable Cause: Failure of the copilot to effect recovery following a poor landing. Failure of the captain to adequately supervise the copilot.
- **3/24/60, Syracuse, N.Y.** — Probable Cause: Failure to establish and maintain runway alignment during touchdown and landing roll. Surface wind condition in excess of that reported and reduced braking because of snow on the runway.
- **3/29/60, Cape Pole, Alaska** — Probable Cause: Misjudged flare-out during a water landing.
- **4/9/60, Fairbanks, Alaska** — Probable Cause: Copilot prematurely retracted the landing gear during the take-off run.

U.S. AIR CARRIER ACCIDENTS (ALL OPERATIONS) 1960

Date	Location	Airline	Type of Service	Type of Airplane	Damage	Total Aboard	Passengers F	S	M/N	Crew F	S	M/N	Other F	S
4/20/60	Hickory, N.C.	PAI	P, S, D	F-27 / Cessna 310	Subst. Dest.	40	0	0	36	0	0	4	4	
	Probable Cause: Pilot of the Cessna, the over-taking aircraft, failed to see and avoid the F-27 during the landing approach.													
5/8/60	Lubbock, Tex.	CAL	P, S, D	Vis 812	None	30	0	0	27	0	0	3	0	1
	Probable Cause: Refueling attendant inadvertently backed into a rotating propeller (seriously injured).													
5/9/60	New York, N.Y.	TWA	P, S, D	B-707	Subst.	109	0	0	100	0	0	9		
	Probable Cause: A poorly conducted instrument approach necessitating a go-around which was initiated too late and improperly executed.													
5/12/60	Miami, Fla.	DAL	P, S, D	DC-8	Minor	51	0	2	42	0	0	7		
	Probable Cause: Turbulence in flight. (Descending through top of a temperature inversion and a zone of vertical wind shear).													
5/21/60	Columbia, S.C.	DAL	F	DC-3	Subst.	2				0	0	2		
	Probable Cause: Failure of crew to exercise adequate caution while parking the aircraft.													
5/23/60	Atlanta, Ga.	DAL	T	CV-880	Dest.	4				4	0	0		
	Probable Cause: The aircraft was stalled, for reasons undetermined, at an altitude too low to effect recovery.													
5/24/60	Denver, Colo.	UAL	P, S, D	DC-8	None	113	0	2	104	0	1	6		
	Probable Cause: Sudden in-flight turbulence.													
5/29/60	Dallas, Texas	TTA	P, S, D	DC-3	None	20	0	0	17	0	1	2		
	Probable Cause: Clear air turbulence.													
6/1/60	Charlotte, N.C.	CAP	P, S, D	DC-6B	None	93	0	1	87	0	0	5		
	Probable Cause: Failure of the injured passengers to comply with the safety instructions. Turbulence.													
6/3/60	Kodiak, Alaska	KOAX	F	G-44	Dest.	1				0	0	1		
	Probable Cause: Pilot failed to raise the landing gear prior to water landing.													
6/14/60	Anaheim, Calif.	LAA	P, S, D	S-55	Subst.	9	0	0	8	0	0	1		
	Probable Cause: Failure of the pilot to properly tighten friction locks on the cyclic control. Failure to maintain manual control of the cyclic control.													
6/14/60	Mt. Gilbert, Alaska	PNA	P, S, I	L-749	Dest.	14	9	0	0	5	0	0		
	Probable Cause: The failure of the crew to use all available navigational aids in establishing the aircraft's position on Amber 1 Airway, thereby allowing the aircraft to deviate from course and fly over hazardous terrain. A contributing factor was the failure of Air Defence Radar, which had been tracking the aircraft, to notify either ARTCC or the crew that the aircraft was proceeding on a dangerous course.													
6/14/60	Chicago, Ill.	UAL	P, S, D	DC-8	Subst.	47	0	0	41	0	0	6		
	Probable Cause: Inability of the pilot to maintain directional control caused by failure of the No. 4 reverse mechanism.													
6/19/60	Dallas, Tex.	AAL	P, S, D	B-707	Subst.	112	0	0	104	0	0	8		
	Probable Cause: Inadvertent actuation of the stabilizer trim switch to the full nose-up position during flare-out and touchdown.													
6/22/60	Newark, N.J.	EAL	P, S, D	L-188	Subst.	54	0	0	48	0	0	6		
	Probable Cause: Improper fit between the tail pipe lower shroud and the tail pipe shroud extension permitting accumulation of fuel which was ignited causing fire damage at an unknown time.													
6/23/60	Dallas, Tex.	CAL	F	DC-7	Subst.	2				0	0	2		
	Probable Cause: Inadvertent gear retraction during landing.													
7/3/60	Nr. Poughkeepsie, N.Y.	UAL	P, S, D	DC-8	None	84	0	1	76	0	0	7		
	Probable Cause: Turbulence in flight. Failure of passengers to comply with seat belt sign and the cabin attendants to insure such compliance.													
7/14/60	Manila, P.I.	NWA	P, S, I	DC-7C	Dest.	58	1	0	50	0	0	7		
	Probable Cause: The internal failure of No. 2 engine, resulting in oil contamination, loss of oil supply, subsequent loss of the No. 2 propeller assembly, and fire in-flight, which necessitated a ditching.													

U.S. AIR CARRIER ACCIDENTS (ALL OPERATIONS) 1960

			Type of			Total	Passengers			Crew			Others		
Date	Location	Airline	Service	Airplane	Damage	Aboard	F	S	M/N	F	S	M/N	F	S	M/N
7/17/60	Los Angeles, Calif.	LAA	P, S, D	S-55	Subst.	8	0	0	7	0	0	1			
	Probable Cause: The pilot failed to assure adequate rotor clearance during taxi. Improper parking of the ground service vehicle. Inadequate space allocation at Gate 18 for existing use.														
7/22/60	Houston, Tex.	TTA	P, S, D	DC-3 DC-7B Parked	Subst.	12	0	0	9	1	0	2			
	Probable Cause: A defective "O" ring in the right landing gear compensating cylinder, resulting in a loss of hydraulic fluid and causing a loss of braking. Judgment in scheduling the aircraft for flight without repairing hydraulic trouble.														
7/22/60	Hawthorne, Calif.	SAS	T	DC-4	Subst.	3				0	0	3			
	Probable Cause: Copilot inadvertently actuated the landing gear control instead of the flap control.														
7/27/60	Forest Park, Ill.	CHA	P, S, D	S-58	Dest.	13	11	0	0	2	0	0			
	Probable Cause: The Board determined N-879 became uncontrollable and crashed as a result of a structural disintegration in flight, initiated by a fatigue fracture of a main rotor blade.														
7/28/60	Avoca, Pa.	AAA	T	CV-440	Subst.	2				0	0	2			
	Probable Cause: Inadequate supervision of the trainee pilot's action by the instructor-pilot during the execution of a go-around following a poorly executed approach.														
8/10/60	Northeast Cape, Alaska	ALA	P, S, I	Beech C-18S	Dest.	6	0	0	5	0	0	1			
	Probable Cause: Loss of directional control during landing in a strong, gusty cross wind. Judgment of the pilot in initiating the flight to Northeast Cape where a known adverse cross wind existed.														
8/13/60	Madison, Wisc.	NCA	P, S, D	DC-3	Subst.	19	0	0	16	0	0	3			
	Probable Cause: Fatigue failure of the left landing gear strut brace fitting, P/N 4341810.														
8/15/60	Nome, Alaska	MUN	P, NS, D	L-10A	Dest.	10	0	0	9	0	0	1	•		
	Probable Cause: Loss of directional control during the landing roll resulting from the pilot's failure to use the proper single engine landing technique.														
8/25/60	Nr. Chanute, Kan.	TWA	P, S, D	L-049	None	53	0	1	47	0	1	4			
	Probable Cause: Severe in-flight turbulence.														
9/6/60	Des Moines, Ia.	OZA	P, S, D	DC-3	Subst.	14	0	0	11	0	0	3			
	Probable Cause: Failure of the right engine, No. 10 cylinder exhaust insert mounting.														
9/7/60	Accra, Ghana, Africa	PAWA	P, S, I	DC-7	None	40	0	0	30	0	0	10	1	0	0
	Probable Cause: Lack of alertness of the ground crewman.														
9/8/60	Texarkana, Ark.	AAL	P, S, D	DC-6A	None	65	0	0	60	0	1	4			
	Probable Cause: In-flight turbulence.														
9/10/60	Atlanta, Ga.	SOU	P, S, D	DC-3, DC-3 Parked	Minor	12	0	0	9	0	0	3			
	Probable Cause: Failure of the pilot and ground personnel to assure adequate separation between aircraft while attempting to maneuver the aircraft in a congested area.														
9/11/60	Washington, D.C.	AAL	P, S, D	CV-240	Subst.	35	0	0	32	0	0	3			
	Probable Cause: Copilot inadvertently actuated the gear lever to the up position after touchdown for landing.														
9/13/60	Minneapolis, Minn.	CAP	P, S, D	Vis 700D	Subst.	45	0	0	41	0	0	4			
	Probable Cause: Failure of the tire tread during takeoff.														
9/14/60	LaGuardia, N.Y.	AAL	P, S, D	L-188	Dest.	76	0	0	70	0	0	6			
	Probable Cause: Failure of the pilot to properly plan and execute the approach to a landing. Factors which may have contributed were the shortened runway and the unmarked upper portion of the dike.														
9/19/60	Guam, Mariana Islands, Agana NAS	WOA	P, MC	DC-6B	Dest.	94	73	9	4	7	1	0			
	Probable Cause: The failure of the pilot to comply with published departure procedures applicable to runways 6 left and 6 right.														
10/1/60	Orlando, Fla.	EAL	P, S, D	M-404 Beech	Subst. Dest.	27	0	0	24	0	0	3		1	
	Probable Cause: Failure of each of the pilots to observe and avoid the other aircraft. Failure of the tower controller to exercise adequate control over aircraft in the traffic pattern.														

U.S. AIR CARRIER ACCIDENTS (ALL OPERATIONS) 1960

Date	Location	Airline	Type of Service	Type of Airplane	Damage	Total Aboard	Passengers F	S	M/N	Crew F	S	M/N	Others F	S	M/N
10/4/60	Boston, Mass.	EAL	P, S, D	L-188	Dest.	72	59	8	0	3	1	1			
	Probable Cause: The unique and critical sequence of the loss and recovery of engine power following bird ingestion, resulting in loss of airspeed and control during takeoff.														
10/4/60	Sacramento, Calif.	COP	C, MC	C-46F	Minor	2				0	0	2			
				Cessna	Dest.	2							2	0	
	Probable Cause: Cessna pilot failed to see the C-46 in time to avoid a collision.														
10/7/60	Newark, N.J.	AAL	P, S, D	DC-6	Subst.	22	0	0	17	0	0	5			
	Probable Cause: Aircraft was landed nose wheel first in a crosswind resulting in overloads and subsequent failure of the nose gear, improper supervision of the landing by the captain.														
10/15/60	Plain City, Utah	COP	C, MC	C-46F	Dest.	2				2	0	0			
	Probable Cause: The fatigue failure of the right wing lower attach angle bolts resulting in an in-flight wing failure.														
10/24/60	Miami, Fla.	ARA	TF	C-46	Subst.	2				0	0	2			
	Probable Cause: Material failure of the left landing gear retract cylinder. Failure for an undetermined reason of the gear to extend to the double lock position using the emergency system.														
10/25/60	Fort Worth, Tex.	AAL	P, S, D	B-707	Subst.	126	0	0	118	0	0	8			
	Probable Cause: Failure of the nose gear to extend for reasons undetermined.														
10/28/60	Missoula, Mont.	NWA	P, S, D	DC-4	Dest.	12	8	0	0	4	0	0			
	Probable Cause: The failure of the pilot to continue in accordance with his IFR flight plan by attempting a VFR approach during instrument weather conditions.														
10/29/60	Toledo, Ohio	APA	P, Public	C-46	Dest.	48	20	10	15	2	0	1			
	Probable Cause: The loss of control during a premature liftoff. Contributing factors were the overweight aircraft, weather conditions, and partial loss of power in the left engine.														
11/3/60	Wilmington, Del.	EAL	P, S, D	M-404	Subst.	41	0	0	38	0	0	3			
	Probable Cause: Loss of directional control during the take-off roll. Inadequate supervision by the captain.														
11/3/60	Eau Claire, Wisc.	NWA	P, S, D	L-188 AF-B47	None.	58	0	1	51	0	0	6			
	Probable Cause: Improper air traffic control procedures.														
11/17/60	Denver, Colo.	UAL	P, S, D	DC-6 / BC-35	Subst. / Subst.	19	0	0	15	0	0	4			
	Probable Cause: Failure of the Bonanza pilot to adhere to traffic patern procedures and to execute an immediate go-around. High level of air traffic in the traffic pattern. Failure of the DC-6 pilots before and during the final approach to see the Bonanza under an adverse condition of sunglare.														
11/28/60	Akiak, Alaska	NC	P, S, D	Cessna T-50	Subst.	2	0	0	1	0	0	1			
	Probable Cause: Hidden hazard in the selected landing area. Failure of the pilot to note the area marked for landing.														
11/28/60	Kotzebue, Alaska	WLA	F	Beech B-18	Minor	1				0	0	1			
	Probable Cause: Misinterpretation by the pilot of unclear signals given by the ground.														
12/3/60	Head of Nichowak River, Alaska	COA	F	PA-18	Subst.	1				0	0	1			
	Probable Cause: Pilot landed on area covered by snow, the condition of which was unsuitable for wheel equipment aircraft.														
12/4/60	Wolbach, Neb.	UAL	P, S, D	B-720	None	91	0	1	83	0	0	7			
	Probable Cause: In-flight turbulence. Inadequate precaution prior to entering an area of possible turbulence.														
12/5/60	Atlanta, Ga.	TWA	P, S, D	L-1049G	Subst.	36	0	0	30	0	0	6			
	Probable Cause: Failure of the No. 3 engine attributed to distress of the No. 2 piston resulting from either piston land or ring failure.														
12/10/60	Golovin, Alaska	MUN	CH	SN	Subst.	3	0	0	2	0	0	1			
	Probable Cause: White-out conditions resulting in loss of visual reference. Pilot attempted to continue VFR flight in IFR conditions.														

U.S. AIR CARRIER ACCIDENTS (ALL OPERATIONS) 1960

Date	Location	Airline	Type of Service	Airplane	Damage	Total Aboard	Passengers			Crew			Others		
							F	S	M/N	F	S	M/N	F	S	M/N
/16/60	Nr. Staten Island, N.Y.	TWA	P, S, D	L-1049	Dest.	44	39	0	0	5	0	0			
		UAL	P, S, D	DC-8	Dest.	84	77	0	0	7	0	0	5		

Probable Cause: United Flight 826 proceeded beyond its clearance limit and the confines of the airspace allocated to the flight by Air Traffic Control. A contributing factor was the high rate of speed of the DC-8 as it approached the Preston intersection, coupled with the change of clearance which reduced the enroute distance along Victor 123 by approximately 11 miles.

| /18/60 | Northeast Cape, Alaska | WLA | P, MC | Beech C-18 | Dest. | 10 | 0 | 8 | 0 | 0 | 2 | 0 | | | |

Probable Cause: Loss of control during take-off climb due to overload condition and improper center of gravity. Judgment of pilot in initiating flight without adequate preflight preparation.

| 2/19/60 | Kodiak Island, Alaska | KOAX | P, S, D | G-21A | Subst. | 4 | 0 | 0 | 3 | 0 | 0 | 1 | | | |

Probable Cause: The pilot failed to see obstruction while taxiing. Unsuitable terrain for operating aircraft.

U.S. AIR CARRIER ACCIDENTS (ALL OPERATIONS) 1961

Date	Location	Airline	Type of Service	Airplane	Damage	Total Aboard	Passengers			Crew			Others		
							F	S	M/N	F	S	M/N	F	S	M/N
6/61	Whittier, Calif.	LAA	P, S, D	S-55	Subst.	3	0	0	2	0	0	1			

Probable Cause: Pilot misjudged clearance distance during landing.

| 9/61 | Over Rockfort, Ill. | CAL | P, S, D | B-707 | Subst. | 24 | 0 | 0 | 16 | 0 | 0 | 8 | | | |

Probable Cause: In-flight engine fire casued by material failure of the No. 1 fuel manifold.

| 14/61 | Chicago, Ill. | UAL | NR | DC-7 | Subst. | 3 | | | | 0 | 0 | 3 | | | |

Probable Cause: Inadvertent retraction of the landing gear by the flight engineer during the landing roll. Malfunction of the landing gear control down lock device permitting inadvertent retraction of the landing gear control.

| 22/61 | Nr. Katy, Tex. | COP | C, MC | C-46F | Dest. | 2 | | | | 2 | 0 | 0 | | | |

Probable Cause: Fatigue failure of the No. 8 cylinder hold down studs causing an uncontrollable in-flight fire.

| 24/61 | Pittsburgh, Pa. | CAP | P, S, D | Vis | Subst. | 47 | 0 | 0 | 44 | 0 | 0 | 3 | | | |

Probable Cause: First Officer misjudged and undershot the landing approach. Inadequate supervision by the captain.

| 28/61 | Montauk Point, L.I., N.Y. | AAL | T | B-707 | Dest. | 6 | | | | 6 | 0 | 0 | | | |

Probable Cause: A loss of control for an undetermined reason.

| 28/61 | Knoxville, Tenn. | CAP | P, S, D | Vis | Subst. | 31 | 0 | 0 | 27 | 0 | 0 | 4 | | | |

Probable Cause: Failure of the left main gear down lock mechanism caused by the interference of foreign material. Malfunction of the left main gear manual indicator caused by improper maintenance and inspection.

| '31/61 | Miami, Fla. | AAT | T | C-46N | Subst. | 3 | | | | 0 | 0 | 3 | | | |

Probable Cause: Pilot failed to extend the landing gear prior to landing. Inadequate supervision by the check pilot. Inoperative condition of the landing gear warning system.

| 6/61 | Dallas, Tex. | DAL | P, S, D | DC-8 | Subst. | 109 | 0 | 0 | 102 | 0 | 0 | 7 | | | |

Probable Cause: Loss of directional control during the landing roll. Excessive speed at touchdown combined with runway conditions causing hydroplaning and a reduction of effective braking.

| '14/61 | Atlanta, Ga. | DAL | T | C-46 | Subst. | 3 | | | | 0 | 0 | 3 | | | |

Probable Cause: Inadvertent actuation of the landing gear control from the down position.

| 15/61 | Nr. Honolulu, Hawaii | PAWA | P, S, I | B-707 | None | 111 | 0 | 1 | 99 | 0 | 0 | 11 | | | |

Probable Cause: Failure of the injured persons to comply with the "Fasten Seat Belt" request. In-flight turbulence.

| '17/61 | Goldsboro, N.C. | PAI | P, S, D | F-27 | Subst. | 24 | 0 | 0 | 21 | 0 | 0 | 3 | | | |

Probable Cause: Fatigue failure of the upper drag strut hinge pin bolt.

| '18/61 | Stuttgart and Nuremberg, West Germany | PAWA | C, S, I | DC-7C | Subst. | 3 | | | | 0 | 0 | 3 | | | |

Probable Cause: Improperly executed instrument approach during which the aircraft was permitted to descend below obstructing terrain before initiating a missed approach. Inadequate supervision by the captain.

U.S. AIR CARRIER ACCIDENTS (ALL OPERATIONS) 1961

							Total	Passengers			Crew			Others		
Date	Location	Airline	Type of Service	Airplane	Damage	Aboard		F	S	M/N	F	S	M/N	F	S	M
2/25/61	Houston, Tex.	BNF	P, S, D	B-720	Subst.	31		0	0	24	0	0	7			
	Probable Cause: Pilot misjudged during the approach resulting in a hard landing short of the runway.															
3/9/61	Nr. Joliet, Ill.	CHA	C, S, D	Bell 47G2	Subst.	1					0	0	1			
	Probable Cause: Failure to properly compensate for adverse in-flight turbulence and for wind conditions during a precautionary landing. Adverse wind conditions.															
3/9/61	Nr. Elgin, Ill.	UAL	P, S, D	DC-6	Subst.	46		0	0	41	0	0	5			
	Probable Cause: In-flight bird strike.															
3/13/61	Cleveland, Ohio	UAL	P, S, D	DC-7	Subst.	51		0	0	46	0	0	5			
	Probable Cause: Material failure of the No. 2 power recovery turbine shaft of the No. 4 engine during the takeoff roll.															
3/20/61	Chicago, Ill.	CHA	P, S, D	S-58C	Subst.	2					0	0	2			
	Probable Cause: Improper maintenance and inspection during preflight inspection.															
3/26/61	St. Louis, Mo.	TWA	P, S, D	B-707	Subst.	125		0	0	117	0	0	8			
	Probable Cause: Pilot misjudged flare-out and failed to maintain adequate airspeed resulting in hard landing short of the runway.															
3/30/61	Las Vegas, Nev.	TWA	F	L-049	Subst.	3					0	0	3			
	Probable Cause: Retraction of the right main landing gear caused by a foreign particle in the landing gear selector valve.															
3/31/61	Crown Mt., Kodiak Island, Alaska	KOAX	P, NS, D	G-44	Dest.	1					0	1	0			
	Probable Cause: Pilot attempted to continue VFR flight in adverse weather conditions at an altitude too low to clear the terrain. Adverse weather and conditions conducive to white-out.															
4/8/61	Shishmarf, Alaska	WLA	P, S, D	Beech C-18S	Subst.	1					0	0	1			
	Probable Cause: Unsuitable landing conditions for landing. Lack of information on field conditions necessary to flight operations.															
4/9/61	Jacksonville, Fla.	EAL	P, S, D	CV-440	Minor	45		0	1	41	0	1	2			
	Probable Cause: In-flight turbulence. Inadequate weather forecast. Failure of the flight crew to ascertain seat belts were properly used.															
4/11/61	New Orleans, La.	NAL	P, S, D	L-188A	Subst.	58		0	0	53	0	0	5			
	Probable Cause: Improper instrument approach procedures and a loss of directional control during the landing roll. Reduced braking caused by water on the runway. Failure of the pilot to discontinue an unsatisfactory instrument approach.															
4/12/61	Chicago, Ill.	DAL	P, S, D	DC-8	Subst.	124		0	0	117	0	0	7			
	Probable Cause: An improperly executed landing approach.															
4/16/61	Detroit, Mich.	DAL	P, S, D	DC-8	Subst.	107		0	0	100	0	0	7			
	Probable Cause: An improprely executed instrument landing approach resulting in descent below terrain obstructions.															
4/17/61	Chicago, Ill.	CHA	C, S, D	Bell 47G	Subst.	1					0	0	1			
	Probable Cause: Pilot failed to see and avoid an obstruction. Judgment of the pilot in maneuvering beyond established limits.															
4/17/61	Chicago, Ill.	NCA	P, S, D	DC-3	Subst.	27		0	0	24	0	0	3			
	Probable Cause: Failure of the truck driver to see, and yield the right of way to the aircraft.															
4/21/61	Downers Grove, Ill.	CHA	C, S, D	Bell 47G	Subst.	1					0	0	1			
	Probable Cause: Loss of control caused by erratic stabilizer damper operation.															
4/25/61	Denver, Colo.	UAL	T	DC-6	Subst.	3					0	0	3			
	Probable Cause: Inadvertent actuation of the landing gear control during the landing roll causing collapse of the nose gear.															
5/9/61	Nr. Vero Beach, Fla.	CAP	P, S, D	DC-6B	None	20		0	0	15	0	1	4			
	Probable Cause: In-flight turbulence.															
5/17/61	Over Springfield, Ill.	DAL	P, S, D	CV-880	Subst.	73		0	0	67	0	0	6			
	Probable Cause: Malfunction of the No. 2 engine starter system for an undetermined reason.															
6/6/61	St. Louis, Mo.	OZA	P, S, D	DC-3	Subst.	16		0	0	13	0	0	3			
	Probable Cause: Brakes failure caused by a loss of hydraulic fluid resulting from a defective "O"ring seal. Failure of the crew to detect the sight gauges indication of an inadequate level of hydraulic fluid. The lack of crew training in emergency procedures for use in the event of brake failure.															

e	Location	Airline	Type of Service	Airplane	Damage	Total Aboard	Passengers F	S	M/N	Crew F	S	M/N	Others F	S	M/N
6/61	Jacksonville, Fla.	DAL	T	CV-880	Subst.	5				0	0	5			
7/61	Durango, Colo.	FAL	P, S, D	CV-340	Subst.	18	0	0	15	0	0	3			
1/61	Kotzebue, Alaska	WLA	P, NS, D	C-46A	Subst.	2				0	0	2			
1/61	Kodiak, Alaska	KOAX	NR	A 7GCB	Subst.	2				0	0	2			
5/61	Patrick AFB, Fla.	USO	C, MT	DC-4	Subst.	2				0	0	2			
6/61	Miami, Fla.	PAWA	T	DC-6B	Subst.	5				0	0	5			
0/61	Alaknuk, Alaska	NC	P, S, D	Cessna T-50	Subst.	3	0	0	2	0	0	1			
/61	Bismarck. N.D.	FAL	P, S, D	DC-3	Subst.	4	0	0	0	0	0	4			
1/61	Denver, Colo.	UAL	P, S, D	DC-8	Dest.	122	17	12	86	0	0	7	1	0	0
3/61	Albany, Ga.	RID	C	C-46	Subst.	2				0	1	1			
9/61	Orlando, Fla.	EAL	P, S, D	DC-7	Subst.	29	0	0	24	0	0	5			
1/61	Dillingham, Alaska	WEA	P, S, D	L-12	Subst.	5	0	0	4	0	0	1			
1/61	Shemya, Alaska	ALA	NS, MC	DC-6	Dest.	6				6	0	0			
4/61	Chicago, Ill.	UAL	P, S, D	DC-8	Dest.	102	0	0	95	0	0	7			
29/61	Los Angeles, Calif.	AAL	P, S, D	B-707	Subst.	52	0	0	44	0	0	8			
3/61	New York, N.Y.	EAL	C, S, I	L-1049G	Dest.	3				0	1	2			

Probable Causes (in order):

Jacksonville, Fla. — Probable Cause: Malfunction of the emergency side of the nose gear emergency extension valve caused by an out of tolerance "O" ring packing.

Durango, Colo. — Probable Cause: Pilots failed to extend the landing gear prior to landing.

Kotzebue, Alaska — Probable Cause: Pilot misjudged the landing approach because of sun glare and reflection. Judgment of the pilot in continuing the approach under known adverse visual conditions.

Kodiak, Alaska — Probable Cause: Puncture of the right float in an undetermined manner.

Patrick AFB, Fla. — Probable Cause: The undetected loss of nose gear side brace attach bolt caused by inadequate maintenance and inspection.

Miami, Fla. — Probable Cause: Fatigue failure of the landing gear up latch release cable. Installation of an improper bolt in the emergency landing gear system.

Alaknuk, Alaska — Probable Cause: Judgment of the pilot in initiating flight operations in adverse wind conditions. Unfavorable wind and water conditions.

Bismarck. N.D. — Probable Cause: First Officer misjudged distance, resulting in an excessively low landing approach. Inadequate supervision and precautionary action by the captain. Failure of the truckdriver to heed the caution sign with appropriate action.

Denver, Colo. — Probable Cause: The asymmetric thrust which, during a hydraulic emergency, resulted from failure of the thrust reversers on engines Nos. 1 and 2 when reverse thrust was selected. A contributing factor was the failure of the first officer to monitor the thrust reverse indicator lights when applying reverse thrust.

Albany, Ga. — Probable Cause: Loss of flying speed and control caused by an adverse wind condition. Judgment of the pilot in initiating takeoff in existing condition.

Orlando, Fla. — Probable Cause: Overload failure of the nose gear caused by an improperly executed level off and touchdown during landing. Unfavorable wind condition and heavy rain associated with a known thunderstorm during landing.

Dillingham, Alaska — Probable Cause: Fire caused by failure of a fuel line connection at the carburetor.

Shemya, Alaska — Probable Cause: The absence of approach and runway lights, and the failure of the GCA controller to give more positive guidance to the pilot during the last stage of his approach.

Chicago, Ill. — Probable Cause: In-flight engine fire caused by material failure of the No. 2 copper brazed joint of the fuel manifold cluster.

Los Angeles, Calif. — Probable Cause: Improperly executed approach and level off by the First Officer and improper recovery from the resultant bounced landing by the captain. Inadequate supervision by the captain.

New York, N.Y. — Probable Cause: Fatigue failure of the upper cap weld of the right landing gear shock strut cylinder.

U.S. AIR CARRIER ACCIDENTS (ALL OPERATIONS) 1961

Date	Location	Airline	Type of Service	Airplane	Damage	Total Aboard	Passengers			Crew			Others	
							F	S	M/N	F	S	M/N	F	S
8/4/61	Nr. Mason City, Iowa	NWA	P, S, D	B-720B	None	49	0	1	41	0	0	7		
	Probable Cause: In-flight turbulence. Inadequate caution by the pilot relative to turbulence. Inadequate company flight advisory procedures.													
8/14/61	Hinchinbrook Island, Alaska	COA	P, S, D	G-44	Subst.	2	0	0	1	0	0	1		
	Probable Cause: Premature flap retraction.													
9/1/61	Chicago, Ill.	TWA	P, S, D	L-049	Dest.	78	73	0	0	5	0	0		
	Probable Cause: The loss of an AN-175-21 nickel steel bolt from the parallelogram linkage of the elevator boost system, resulting in loss of control of the aircraft.													
9/4/61	San Antonio, Tex.	EAL	P, S, D	DC-7	Subst.	25	0	0	20	0	0	5		
	Probable Cause: Inadvertent actuation of the landing gear control to the up position during the landing roll.													
9/4/61	Baltimore, Md.	NEA	P, S, D	Vis	Subst.	23	0	0	19	0	0	4		
	Probable Cause: Malfunction of the left gear up lock caused by an improperly secured clevis pin.													
9/10/61	Shannon, Ireland	PRE	P, Public	DC-6	Dest.	83	77	0	0	6	0	0		
	Investigation conducted by the Irish Government.													
9/16/61	New York, N.Y.	PAWA	P, S, I	DC-8	Subst.	133	0	0	124	0	0	9		
	Probable Cause: Unwanted asymmetrical reverse thrust resulting from malfunction of the Nos. 3 and 4 reversers caused by the deteriorated condition of the "O" ring seal in the Nos. 3 and 4 reverse ejector valves. Improper crew execution of the checklist established for the existing emergency condition. Faulty design features of the aircraft hydraulic systems.													
9/17/61	Chicago, Ill.	NWA	P, S, D	L-188C	Dest.	37	32	0	0	5	0	0		
	Probable Cause: Mechanical failure in the aileron primary control system due to an improper replacement of the aileron boost assembly, resulting in a loss of lateral control of the aircraft at an altitude too low to effect recovery.													
9/20/61	Portland, Oregon	FTLX	C	L-1049	None	3				0	0	0		
	Probable Cause: Inattention of the ground crewman to the rotating propeller and failure to follow established walk patterns.													
9/23/61	Kansas City, Mo.	DAL	P, S, D	CV-340	Subst.	12	0	0	9	0	0	3		
	Probable Cause: Pilot misjudged level off and failed to make proper recovery from a bounced landing. Unfavorable wind conditions and limited visibility in heavy rain during a critical phase of landing.													
9/24/61	Boston, Mass.	AAL	P, S, D	B-720B	Subst.	71	0	0	63	0	0	8		
	Probable Cause: The captain's decision to land in variable weather conditions precluding adequate orientation relative to location along the runway. A contributing factor was the failure to provide the flight with information concerning the deterioration of runway visual range values.													
9/26/61	Norfolk, Va.	OVN	F	DC-7	Subst.	5				0	0	5		
	Probable Cause: Loss of directional control during the landing roll caused by improper use of propeller reversing and braking. The Captain's inadequate familiarity with the aircraft systems and procedures under normal system hydraulic failure. Failure of the hydraulic system for an undetermined reason.													
10/4/61	Lemont, Ill.	CHA	C, S, D	Bell 47G2	Dest.	1				1	0	0		
	Probable Cause: In-flight failure of the bearing end fitting of the blue rotor blade pitch control link caused by improper bearing alignment at installation.													
10/8/61	Avalon, Calif.	AVA	P, S, D	G21	Dest.	10	0	0	9	0	0	1		
	Probable Cause: Failure of the pilot to make the take-off into the wind under adverse weather condition.													
10/10/61	Des Moines, Ia.	BNF	P, S, D	CV-340	Subst.	34	0	0	3	0	0	3		
	Probable Cause: Improper landing technique which included premature propeller reversal causing a hard bounced landing.													
10/11/61	Seattle, Wash.	WAL	P, S, I	B-720B	Subst.	28	0	0	21	0	0	7		
	Probable Cause: Improper security of the cowling attachment following maintenance inspection.													
10/16/61	Fort Worth, Tex.	BNF	P, S, D	L-188	Subst.	49	0	0	44	0	0	5		
	Probable Cause: Improper adjustment of the right landing gear door actuating mechanism caused by inadequate maintenance and maniteance procedures.													

U.S. AIR CARRIER ACCIDENTS (ALL OPERATIONS) 1961

Date	Location	Airline	Type of Service	Airplane	Damage	Total Aboard	Passengers			Crew			Others		
							F	S	M/N	F	S	M/N	F	S	M/N
10/16/61	Windsor Locks, Conn.	MOH	P, S, D	CV-240	Subst.	16	0	0	13	0	0	3			

Probable Cause: Failure of both pilots to extend the landing gear prior to landing. Improper use of the checklist.

| 10/20/61 | Chicago, Ill. | AAL | P, S, D | B-707 | Subst. | 99 | 0 | 0 | 91 | 0 | 0 | 8 | | | |

Probable Cause: Temporary deformation of the oleo strut packing rings permitting a discharge of hydraulic fluid on the right brake assemblies.

| 10/24/61 | Prince of Wales Island, Alaska | ELL | P, S, D | G-21 | Subst. | 6 | 0 | 0 | 5 | 0 | 0 | 1 | | | |

Probable Cause: Hidden hazard in the landing area.

| 11/1/61 | Tuscaloosa, Ala. | SOU | P, S, D | DC-3 Cessna 172 | Subst. | 23 | 0 | 0 | 20 | 0 | 0 | 3 | | | |

Probable Cause: Captain misjudged clearance distance during taxi.

| 11/5/61 | Nr. Alban, N.Y. | TWA | P, S, D | B-720B | Subst. | 42 | 0 | 0 | 34 | 0 | 0 | 8 | | | |

Probable Cause: Oil starvation of the No. 2 bearing which caused its failure. This precipitated the fracture of the low-pressure rear hub and the overspeeding and subsequent disintegration of the low-pressure turbine section.

| 11/8/61 | Richmond, Va. | IMP | P, MC | L-049 | Dest. | 79 | 74 | 0 | 0 | 2 | 0 | 3 | | | |

Probable Cause: The lack of command coordination and decision, lack of judgment, and lack of knowledge resulting in loss of power in three engines creating an emergency situation which the crew could not handle.

| 11/11/61 | Nr. Wrangell, Alaska | ACL | P, S, D | G-21A | Subst. | 8 | 0 | 0 | 7 | 0 | 0 | 1 | | | |

Probable Cause: Material failure of the cam reduction gear assembly.

| 11/13/61 | Nr. Annette, Alaska | NWA | P, MC, I | DC-7C | None | 101 | 0 | 2 | 93 | 0 | 0 | 6 | | | |

Probable Cause: Sudden adverse air condition.

| 11/14/61 | Nr. Galena, Alaska | WLA | P, S, D | Cessna 180B | Subst. | 2 | 0 | 0 | 1 | 0 | 0 | 1 | | | |

Probable Cause: Power failure caused by improper use of carburetor heat. Judgment of the pilot in attempting continued visual flight under existing condition of weather and aircraft equipment.

| 11/15/61 | Boston, Mass. | NAL | P, S, D | DC-6B | Subst. | 30 | 0 | 0 | 25 | 0 | 0 | 5 | | | |
| | | NEA | | Vis | Subst. | 45 | 0 | 0 | 37 | 0 | 0 | 8 | | | |

Probable Cause: The ground collision accident occurred as the result of commencement of takeoff by National 429 without clearance. Contributing factors were the failure of tower personnel to provide adequate surveillance of the active runway and to issue an appropriate warning message to the pilot of National 429 alerting him to the impending traffic confliction.

| 11/19/61 | Nr. Bristol, Tenn. | PAI | P, S, D | DC-3 | Subst. | 9 | 0 | 0 | 6 | 0 | 0 | 3 | | | |

Probable Cause: Pilot descended to an altitude below obstructing terrain caused by an improperly executed instrument approach. Lack of attention by the pilots and inadequate supervision by the captain.

| 11/23/61 | Morgantown, W. Va. | LCA | P, S, D | DC-3 | Subst. | 14 | 0 | 0 | 11 | 0 | 0 | 3 | | | |

Probable Cause: Loss of directional control during the landing roll caused by touchdown at excessive speed and reduced braking resulting from the wet runway condition.

| 11/25/61 | Las Vegas, Nev. | PAC | P, S, D | F-27 | Subst. | 27 | 0 | 0 | 24 | 0 | 0 | 3 | | | |

Probable Cause: Jamming of the nose gear actuating mechanism caused by a rag left in the nosewheel compartment.

| 12/1/61 | Grand Island, Neb. | FTLX | C | L-1049H | Subst. | 4 | | | | 0 | 0 | 4 | | | |

Probable Cause: Unsuitable ramp condition caused by inadequate inspection and maintenance.

| 12/2/61 | Jacksonville, Fla. | DAL | P, S, D | DC-7B | Subst. | 20 | 0 | 0 | 15 | 0 | 0 | 5 | | | |

Probable Cause: The pilot's improper execution of an instrument approach.

| 12/5/61 | New Castle, Del. | AAL | P, S, D | L-188 | None | 50 | 0 | 0 | 45 | 0 | 1 | 4 | | | |

Probable Cause: In-flight turbulence.

| 12/6/61 | Port Wakefield, Alaska | KOAX | NS | G-44 | None | 1 | | | | 0 | 0 | 1 | 0 | 1 | 0 |

Probable Cause: Inattention of the bystander to the rotating propeller.

U.S. AIR CARRIER ACCIDENTS (ALL OPERATIONS) 1961

Date	Location	Airline	Type of Service	Airplane	Damage	Total Aboard	Passengers			Crew			Others		
							F	S	M/N	F	S	M/N	F	S	M
12/8/61	Nr. Nome, Alaska	WLA	P, S, D	Cessna 180B	Dest.	2	1	0	0	1	0	0			
	Probable Cause: Loss of control caused by attempted continued flight in adverse weather conditions. Judgment of the pilot in continuing the flight into known adverse weather conditions. Desire of the pilot to complete the flight because of the emergency condition of the passenger.														
12/20/61	Nr. Pittsburgh, Pa.	AAL	P, S, D	B-707	None	114	0	0	106	0	1	7			
	Probable Cause: Failure of the pilots of each aircraft to maintain sufficient visual reference to the other's aircraft and alter course to assure the avoidance of near collision.														
12/24/61	Old Harbor, Kodiak Island, Alaska	KOAX	P, S, D	G21A	Dest.	5	1	0	3	0	0	1			
	Probable Cause: An improperly executed takeoff which resulted in an inadvertent descent into the water. This produced a high speed, low angle porpoise from which the pilot was unable to recover.														

U.S. AIR CARRIER ACCIDENTS (ALL OPERATIONS) 1962

Date	Location	Airline	Type of Service	Airplane	Damage	Total Aboard	Passengers			Crew			Others		
							F	S	M/N	F	S	M/N	F	S	M
1/1/62	Charlotte, N.C.	PAI	P, S, D	F-27	Subst.	36	0	0	33	0	0	3			
	Probable Cause: Collapse of the landing gear caused by an electrical short in the landing gear selector valve connector plug.														
1/13/62	Fillmore, Calif.	UAL	P, S, D	DC-6	None	52	0	0	47	0	1	4			
	Probable Cause: In-flight turbulence.														
1/14/62	Birmingham, Ala.	EAL	P, S, D	L-188	Subst.	30	0	0	25	0	0	5			
	Probable Cause: Pilots failed to extend the landing gear prior to landing. Inadequate use of the before landing checklist.														
1/16/62	Limestone, Me.	RID	TF	C-46	Subst.	2	0	0	0	0	0	2			
	Probable Cause: Inadvertent feathering of the No. 1 propeller during intended feathering of the No. 2 propeller by the copilot. Inadequate battery condition caused by inadequate maintenance and inspection.														
1/20/62	Big Tree, Calif.	BLA	P, D	DC-3	Minor	22	0	3	16	0	0	3			
	Probable Cause: In-flight turbulence. Failure of the affected passengers to properly fasten seat belts.														
1/20/62	Chicago, Ill.	UAL	P, S, D	DC-7	Subst.	26	0	0	21	0	0	5			
		AAL		CV-240	Subst.	35	0	0	32	0	0	3			
	Probable Cause: Failure of the pilot of N-94253 to exercise adequate caution while taxiing under adverse conditions. Poor braking action on icy runway.														
1/26/62	Detroit, Mich.	AAL	C, S, D	DC-7	Subst.	3	0	0	0	0	0	3			
	Probable Cause: Failure for an undetermined reason of the right nose gear bulkhead fitting of the nose gear retracting link axis tube.														
1/26/62	Fort Lauderdale, Fla.	NWA	P, S, D	B-720B	Subst.	9	0	0	2	0	0	7			
	Probable Cause: Pilot misjudged distance and undershot during landing.														
2/1/62	Portland, Ore.	UAL	P, S, D	B-720	Subst.	49	0	0	42	0	0	7			
	Probable Cause: Engine failure caused by fatigue failure of three third stage compressor blades.														
2/3/62	New York, N.Y.	UAL	P, S, D	DC-8	Subst.	125	0	0	117	0	0	8			
	Probable Cause: Judgment of the captain in initiating landing under the existing runway and surface wind conditions. Excessive speed at touchdown and improper minimum distance stopping technique. Unfavorable braking runway conditions.														
2/3/62	Chicago, Ill.	EAL	P, S, D	DC-7	Subst.	60	0	0	55	0	0	5			
	Probable Cause: Pilot failed to use adequate caution during taxi turnoff after landing. Unfavorable runway conditions.														
2/15/62	Nyac, Alaska	NC	CB	Cessna 180A	Subst.	2	0	0	1	0	0	1			
	Probable Cause: Pilot misjudged distance and undershot during landing. Whiteout condition. Failure of the pilot of the aircraft initially damaged to report a hazardous condition.														
2/25/62	Waterloo, Ia.	OZA	P, S, D	F-27	Subst.	21	0	0	18	0	0	3			
	Probable Cause: Loss of directional control during the landing roll caused by deep and drifted snow on one side of the runway. Inadequate runway inspection.														

AIR CARRIER ACCIDENTS (ALL OPERATIONS) 1962

			Type of			Total	Passengers			Crew			Others		
	Location	Airline	Service	Airplane	Damage	Aboard	F	S	M/N	F	S	M/N	F	S	M/N
7/62	Burbank, Calif.	FLTX	F	Can CL-44	Subst.	10	0	0	6	0	0	4			

Probable Cause: Failure of the high pressure turbine bearing caused by oil starvation.

	Location	Airline	Service	Airplane	Damage	Aboard	F	S	M/N	F	S	M/N	F	S	M/N
62	Jamaica Bay, N.Y.	AAL	P, S, D	B707/123B	Dest.	95	87	0	0	8	0	0			

Probable Cause: A rudder control system malfunction producing yaw, sideslips, and roll leading to a loss of control from which recovery action was not effective.

	Location	Airline	Service	Airplane	Damage	Aboard	F	S	M/N	F	S	M/N	F	S	M/N
62	Moses Pt., Alaska	WLA	P, S, D	Beech D-18	Dest.	3	0	1	1	0	0	1			

Probable Cause: Altimeter error for an undetermined reason resulting in descent below obstructing terrain during a visual landing approach. Judgment of the pilot in continuing a visual approach in weather conditions and whiteout which prevent the visual requirements necessary to the type approach being made.

	Location	Airline	Service	Airplane	Damage	Aboard	F	S	M/N	F	S	M/N	F	S	M/N
62	Buffalo, N.Y.	AAL	P, S, D	DC-6	Subst.	56	0	0	51	0	0	5			

Probable Cause: Fatigue failure of the right main landing gear oleo strut during landing.

	Location	Airline	Service	Airplane	Damage	Aboard	F	S	M/N	F	S	M/N	F	S	M/N
5/62	Adak, Alaska	FTLX	C, MC, I	L-1049H	Dest.	7	0	0	0	1	0	6			

Probable Cause: The pilot's misjudgment of distance and altitude during the final approach for landing.

	Location	Airline	Service	Airplane	Damage	Aboard	F	S	M/N	F	S	M/N	F	S	M/N
5/62	Disappeared between Guam and Philippine Is.	FTLX	P, MC, I	L-1049	Dest.	107	96	0	0	11	0	~0			

Probable Cause: Unable to determine the probable cause of this accident from the evidence now available.

	Location	Airline	Service	Airplane	Damage	Aboard	F	S	M/N	F	S	M/N	F	S	M/N
62	Mexico City, Mex.	PAWA	P, S, I	DC-8	Subst.	107	0	0	98	0	0	9			

Probable Cause: Under the jurisdiction of the Mexican Government.

	Location	Airline	Service	Airplane	Damage	Aboard	F	S	M/N	F	S	M/N	F	S	M/N
/62	Shungnak, Alaska	WLA	C, S, D	Cessna 180	Subst.	1	0	0	0	0	0	1			

Probable Cause: Overload failure of the right ski caused by impact with a hidden hazard on the landing area.

	Location	Airline	Service	Airplane	Damage	Aboard	F	S	M/N	F	S	M/N	F	S	M/N
4/62	Wake Island, Pacific Ocean	SLIX	C, MC, I	CL-44	Subst.	6	0	0	4	0	0	2			

Probable Cause: Pilot misjudged distance and undershot during landing.

	Location	Airline	Service	Airplane	Damage	Aboard	F	S	M/N	F	S	M/N	F	S	M/N
7/62	Lompoc, Calif.	PAC	P, S, D	M-404	Subst.	41	0	0	38	0	0	3			

Detachment of the left landing gear jury strut lock assembly bolt.

	Location	Airline	Service	Airplane	Damage	Aboard	F	S	M/N	F	S	M/N	F	S	M/N
8/62	Dallas, Tex.	PUR	TF	DC-3	Dest.	3	0	0	0	3	0	0			

Probable Cause: Pilot failed to maintain flying speed during an improperly executed takeoff and takeoff climb. Judgment of the pilot in initiating the flight and the vice president and general manager for approving the flight under existing circumstances.

	Location	Airline	Service	Airplane	Damage	Aboard	F	S	M/N	F	S	M/N	F	S	M/N
7/62	Manila, Philippines	PAWA	P, S, I	B-707-321	Subst.	53	0	0	43	0	0	10			

Probable Cause: Pilot misjudged distance and undershot during landing. Inadequate supervision by the captain.

	Location	Airline	Service	Airplane	Damage	Aboard	F	S	M/N	F	S	M/N	F	S	M/N
7/62	New York, N.Y.	NEA	P, S, D	Vis	Subst.	27	0	0	23	0	0	4			

Probable Cause: Pilot misjudged speed and distance resulting in an overshoot during landing. A false fire warning caused by malfunction of a fire detection system undergoing service test.

	Location	Airline	Service	Airplane	Damage	Aboard	F	S	M/N	F	S	M/N	F	S	M/N
/62	Ackerly, Tex.	SLIX	C, MC, D	DC-4	Subst.	2	0	0	0	0	0	2			

Probable Cause: Failure of the Nos. 1 and 3 engines under adverse weight and weather conditions resulting in the aircraft being unable to maintain flight.

	Location	Airline	Service	Airplane	Damage	Aboard	F	S	M/N	F	S	M/N	F	S	M/N
2/62	Unionville, Mo.	CAL	P, S, D	B-707	Dest.	45	37	0	0	8	0	0			

Probable Cause: The disintegrating force of a dynamite explosion which occurred in the right rear lavatory, resulting in destruction of the aircraft.

	Location	Airline	Service	Airplane	Damage	Aboard	F	S	M/N	F	S	M/N	F	S	M/N
4/62	Panama City, Fla.	RID	C, MC, D	C-46	Subst.	2	0	0	0	0	0	2			

Probable Cause: Loss of control during landing caused by improper loading.

	Location	Airline	Service	Airplane	Damage	Aboard	F	S	M/N	F	S	M/N	F	S	M/N
8/62	New York, N.Y.	EAL	P, S, D	L-1049	Subst.	40	0	0	35	0	0	5			

Probable Cause: Failure of the bolt attaching the nose gear to the nose gear retract cylinder.

U.S. AIR CARRIER ACCIDENTS (ALL OPERATIONS) 1962

Date	Location	Airline	Type of Service	Airplane	Damage	Total Aboard	Passengers F	Passengers S	Passengers M/N	Crew F	Crew S	Crew M/N	Others F	Others S	Others M/N
6/5/62	San Juan, P.R.	RID	C, S, I	C-46R	Subst.	2	0	0	0	0	0	2			
6/8/62	Miami, Fla.	EAL	T	DC-7	Subst.	4	0	0	0	0	0	4			
6/14/62	Marco, Fla.	PAWA	P, S, I	DC-8	None	47	0	1	37	0	0	9			
6/15/62	San Juan, P.R.	PAWA	P, S, I	B-707-121	None	89	0	0	82	0	1	6			
7/2/62	Wilmington, Del.	COP	T	AW-650	Subst.	6	0	0	0	0	0	6			
7/5/62	Clear AFB, Alaska	ALA	P, S, D	Beech C-18S	Subst.	6	0	0	5	0	0	1			
7/6/62	Vandenburg AFB, Calif.	ZATX	C, MC, D	C-46	Minor	2	0	0	0	0	0	2			
7/7/62	Kotzebue, Alaska	WLA	C, NS, D	Beech C-18S	Subst.	2	0	0	0	0	0	2			
7/8/62	Amarillo, Tex.	CAL	P, S, D	Vis 812	Dest.	16	0	0	13	0	0	3			
7/11/62	Pit-a-Pitre, French W.I.	SAT	C, NS, I	C-46	Subst.	2	0	0	0	0	0	2			
7/17/62	Catalina Island, Calif.	AVA	P, S, D	G-21A	Subst.	7	0	0	6	0	0	1			
7/23/62	Rome, N.Y.	COP	C, MC, D	AR	Subst.	3	0	0	0	0	0	3			
7/26/62	Amsterdam, Holland	PAWA	—	B707	Minor	88	0	10	69	0	2	7			
8/6/62	Rocky Mount, N.C.	PAI	P, S, D	M-404	Subst.	24	0	0	20	0	0	4			
8/6/62	Knoxville, Tenn.	AAL	P, S, D	L-188	Subst.	72	0	0	67	0	0	5			
8/10/62	Clark AFB, P.I.	TRI	C, MC, I	L-1049	Subst.	6	0	0	4	0	0	2			
8/11/62	Liz "A" Alaska	WLA	P, NS, D	Beech AT-11	Subst.	3	0	0	2	0	0	1			
8/17/62	Miami, Fla.	RID	T	C-46R	Subst.	4	0	0	0	0	0	4			

Probable Causes:

- **6/5/62 San Juan, P.R.** — Fatigue failure of the left landing gear side brace caused by improper machining of the component.
- **6/8/62 Miami, Fla.** — Inadequate and premature signalling of ground personnel before and during taxi departure from the terminal gate. Inadequate vigilance and caution of the pilots.
- **6/14/62 Marco, Fla.** — Failure of the crew to anticipate turbulence and turn on the "Fasten Seat Belt" sign. In-flight turbulence.
- **6/15/62 San Juan, P.R.** — Failure of the pilots of both aircrafts to observe the other aircraft in time to avoid the necessity of an extreme collision evasive maneuver.
- **7/2/62 Wilmington, Del.** — Fatigue failure of the right landing gear lower drag strut fitting.
- **7/5/62 Clear AFB, Alaska** — Pilot failed to see and avoid the parked aircraft during initial taxi.
- **7/6/62 Vandenburg AFB, Calif.** — Pilot failed to see and avoid a parked aircraft while taxiing for takeoff.
- **7/7/62 Kotzebue, Alaska** — Inadvertent retraction of the landing gear during takeoff caused by inadequate pre-flight inspection and pre-flight check.
- **7/8/62 Amarillo, Tex.** — The Captain's diversion of his attention during takeoff which allowed the aircraft to settle to the runway striking the Nos. 2 and 3 propellers.
- **7/11/62 Pit-a-Pitre, French W.I.** — Under the jurisdiction of the French Government.
- **7/17/62 Catalina Island, Calif.** — Fatigue failure of the No. 3 propeller blade resulting from vibration caused by rotation of the blade within the retention clamp.
- **7/23/62 Rome, N.Y.** — A wheels-up landing caused by the failure of the normal and malfunction of the emergency landing gear extension systems.
- **7/26/62 Amsterdam, Holland** — Under the jurisdiction of the Netherlands Government.
- **8/6/62 Rocky Mount, N.C.** — Pilot misjudged speed and distance during the landing approach, resulting in an undershoot and hard landing.
- **8/6/62 Knoxville, Tenn.** — The loss of directional control as a result of the improper technique employed in a crosswind landing in adverse weather conditions.
- **8/10/62 Clark AFB, P.I.** — Under the jurisdiction of the Philippine Government.
- **8/11/62 Liz "A" Alaska** — Pilot failed to extend the landing gear for landing.
- **8/17/62 Miami, Fla.** — Loss of directional control and misuse of braking during the landing roll of a bounced landing. Inadequate supervision by the check-pilot.

U.S. AIR CARRIER ACCIDENTS (ALL OPERATIONS) 1962

Date	Location	Airline	Type of Service	Airplane	Damage	Total Aboard	Passengers F	S	M/N	Crew F	S	M/N	Others F	S	M/N
8/22/62	Wilmington, N.C.	PAI	T	M-404	Dest.	3	0	0	0	0	0	3			
	Probable Cause: Unwanted propeller reversal during a critical phase of landing caused by a malfunction of the propeller low pitch stop lever assembly, resulting from foreign matter in the servo valve control.														
8/30/62	New Orleans, La.	EAL	P, S, D	B-720	Subst.	43	0	0	35	0	0	8			
	Probable Cause: Pilot misjudged distance and undershot during landing.														
9/11/62	Cleveland, Ohio	UAL	P, S, D	Car	Subst.	64	0	0	59	0	0	5			
	Probable Cause: Failure of the right nosewheel bearing assembly caused by inadequate maintenance and inspection.														
9/19/62	Daytona Beach, Fla.	EAL	P, S, D	DC-7B	Subst.	16	0	0	11	0	0	5			
	Probable Cause: Improper recovery technique from asymmetrical reverse thrust during the landing roll. Asymmetrical thrust for an undetermined reason under wet runway conditions.														
9/21/62	Miami, Fla.	EAL	P, S, D	B-720	Subst.	20	0	0	13	0	0	7			
	Probable Cause: Pilot misjudged level off and made improper recovery from the resultant bounced landing. Unfavorable wind conditions.														
9/23/62	Albany, N.Y.	UAL	P, S, D	B-720	None	107	0	1	99	0	1	6			
	Probable Cause: Failure of the Captain to take timely turbulence flight precautionary measures in an area of reported turbulence.														
9/23/62	North Atlantic Ocean	FTLX	P, MC, I	L-1049H	Dest.	76	23	0	45	5	0	3			
	Probable Cause: The failure of two of the aircraft's four engines, and improper action of the flight engineer which disabled a third engine, thereby necessitating a ditching at sea.														
10/1/62	Pow "B" Dew Line Site, Alaska.	WLA	P, S, D	Beech C-18S	Subst	5	0	0	4	0	0	1			
	Probable Cause: Pilot misjudged distance and undershot during the landing. Inadequate maintenance and inspection.														
10/3/62	Baltimore, Md.	PAI	P, S, D	M-404	Minor	13	0	0	10	0	0	3	0	1	0
	Probable Cause: Pilot failed to assure that the taxiway was clear before commencing to taxi. The lack of company instructions for the proper dispatching procedures to be used with the type aircraft involved.														
10/14/62	Sacramento, Calif.	UAL	P, S, D	DC-7	Subst.	38	0	0	33	0	0	5			
	Probable Cause: High frequency fatigue failure of the vertical stabilizer, resulting from flutter induced through failure of the Station 135 rudder attachment and bearing assembly caused by inadequate lubrication and inspection.														
10/19/62	Windsor Locks, Conn.	AAA	P, S, D	CV-440	Minor	52	0	0	48	1	0	3			
	Probable Cause: An undetected insecure latching of the rear service door, resulting in an in-flight explosive decompression which ejected a hostess from the aircraft.														
10/22/62	Sitka Sound, Alaska	NWA	P, MC, I	DC-7C	Dest.	102	0	0	95	0	0	7			
	Probable Cause: An uncontrollable overspeeding propeller due to failure in the blower section of the No. 2 engine.														
10/24/62	Pierre, S.D.	NCA	P, S, D	CV-340	Subst.	47	0	0	44	0	0	3			
	Probable Cause: In-flight bird strike during cruising flight at night.														
10/29/62	LaPaz, Bolivia	PGA	P, S, I	DC-7B	Subst.	42	0	0	36	0	0	6			
	Probable Cause: Under the jurisdiction of the Bolivian Government.														
11/9/62	Kingston, Jamaica	PAWA	P, S, I	B-707	None	21	0	0	13	0	1	7			
	Probable Cause: Under the jurisdiction of the British Colony of Jamaica.														
11/23/62	Ellicott City, Md.	UAL	P, S, D	Vis	Dest.	17	13	0	0	4	0	0			
	Probable Cause: A loss of control following separation of the left horizontal stabilizer which had been weakened by a collision with a whistling swan.														
11/30/62	New York, N.Y.	EAL	P, S, D	DC-7	Dest.	51	21	12	12	4	2	0			
	Probable Cause: The technique employed by the crew during abandonment of the approach under fog conditions not adequately reported.														

U.S. AIR CARRIER ACCIDENTS (ALL OPERATIONS) 1962

Date	Location	Airline	Service	Airplane	Damage	Total Aboard	Passengers			Crew			Others		
							F	S	M/N	F	S	M/N	F	S	M
12/4/62	Macon, Ga.	RID	T	C-46A	Subst.	2	0	0	0	0	0	2			
	Probable Cause: Loss of normal system hydraulic fluid caused by improper positioning of the emergency up-lock release handle. Malfunction of the lift landing gear position light and gear warning horn microswitches caused by inadequate maintenance and inspection.															
12/10/62	Los Angeles, Calif.	UAL	P, S, D	DC-6	Subst.	9	0	0	4	0	0	5			
	Probable Cause: Inadvertent landing gear retraction during the landing roll caused by misuse of controls by the flight engineer.															
12/14/62	Hollywood, Calif.	FTLX	C, S, D	L-1049H	Dest.	5	2	0	0	3	0	0	3	0	0
	Probable Cause: The incapacitation of the pilot-in-command, at a critical point in the approach, resulting in a loss of control of the aircraft from which the copilot was unable to recover.															
12/21/62	Grand Island, Neb.	FAL	P, S, D	CV-340	Dest.	42	0	0	9	0	1	2			
	Probable Cause: Failure of the crew to monitor altitude properly during a landing approach.															
12/22/62	Clinton, Iowa	OZA	P, S, D	DC-3	Subst.	26	0	0	23	0	0	3			
	Probable Cause: Pilot misjudged speed and distance and overshot during landing on terrain which was unsuitable under the existing conditions.															

U.S. AIR CARRIER ACCIDENTS (ALL OPERATIONS) 1963

Date	Location	Airline	Service	Airplane	Damage	Total Aboard	Passengers			Crew			Others		
							F	S	M/N	F	S	M/N	F	S	M
1/1/63	Nr. Chicago, Ill.	TWA	S, D	CV-880	Subst.	64	0	0	56	0	0	8			
	Probable Cause: In-flight failure of the nose cowl tension latch.															
1/13/63	Memphis, Tenn.	DAL	F	DC-7	Subst.	5				1	2	2			
		USAF		C-123B	Subst.	0									
	Probable Cause: The crew's inattention to duty while taxiing on an unfamiliar taxiway at night and the captain's failure to stop the aircraft in sufficient time to avoid striking a parked aircraft.															
1/14/63	Tampa, Fla.	DAL	P, S, D	DC-8-12	Subst.	53	0	0	46	0	0	7			
	Probable Cause: Material failure of the left landing gear strut cylinder during landing. Inadequate overhaul and overhaul inspection of the landing gear assembly.															
1/14/63	Barter Island, Alaska	WLA	P, NS, D	Beech AT-11	Dest.	6	4	1	0	1	0	0			
	Probable Cause: Pilot descended below obstructing terrain while attempting a visual landing approach in darkness and adverse weather.															
1/17/63	Bethel, Alaska	NC	P, S, D	Cessna T-50	Subst.	5	0	0	4	0	0	1			
	Probable Cause: Pilot misjudged distance and overshot during an emergency single-engine landing, other unfavorable wind and runway conditions. Unwanted feathering of the left propeller caused by inadequate maintenance and inspection.															
1/17/63	Salt Lake City, Utah	WCA	T/Check	F-27	Dest.	3				3	0	0			
	Probable Cause: The crew's lack of vigilance, for undetermined reasons, in not checking the descent before striking the water.															
1/22/63	Nr. Bakersfield, Calif.	UAL	P, S, D	DC-8	Subst.	65	0	1	57	0	0	7			
	Probable Cause: Failure of the pilots to see the other's aircraft in time to avoid an evasive maneuver.															
1/24/63	Honolulu, Hawaii	HAL	C, S, D	DC-3C	Subst.	2				0	0	2			
	Probable Cause: Failure of the pilots to see and avoid the truck during taxi. Improper use of the taxiway by the truck driver.															
1/29/63	Kansas City, Mo.	CAL	P, S, D	Vis 812	Dest.	8	5	0	0	3	0	0			
	Probable Cause: An undetected accretion of ice on the horizontal stabilizer which, in conjunction with a specified airspeed and aircraft configuration, caused a loss of pitch control.															

U.S. AIR CARRIER ACCIDENTS (ALL OPERATIONS) 1963

Date	Location	Airline	Type of Service	Airplane	Damage	Total Aboard	Passengers F	S	M/N	Crew F	S	M/N	Others F	S	M/N
2/3/63	San Francisco, Calif.	SLIX	C, S, D	L-1049H	Dest.	8	2	3	0	2	1	0			
2/7/63	Nr. Mt. Hamilton, Calif.	WAL	P, S, D	DC-6B	None	38	0	0	33	0	1	4			
2/12/63	Nr. Miami, Fla.	NWA	P, S, D	B720B	Dest.	43	35	0	0	8	0	0			
2/16/63	Puyallup, Wash.	ZATX	C, MC	C-46F	Dest.	2				0	2	0			
3/12/63	Boston, Mass.	EAL	P, S, D	DC-7B	Subst.	20	0	0	15	0	0	5			
3/16/63	Oakland, Calif.	AAL	P, S, D	DC-7B	Subst.	44	0	0	39	0	0	5			
3/18/63	Peoria, Ill.	OZA	P, S, D	DC-3	Subst.	15	0	0	12	0	0	3			
3/25/63	Nr. Panama City, Panama	BNF	P, S, I	B707-227	None	57	0	0	50	0	1	6			
4/2/63	Savoonga, Alaska	WLA	P, S, D	DHC-2	Subst.	2	0	0	1	0	0	1			
4/10/63	Nr. McIntire Pt., Alaska	WLA	P, NS, D	Cessna 180A	Subst.	2	0	0	1	0	0	1			
4/18/63	NE of Des Moines, Iowa	TWA	P, S, D	B707-131B	None	95	0	0	87	0	1	7			
5/8/63	Newark, N.J.	AAA	T	CV-340/440	Subst.	2				0	0	2			
5/15/63	Miami, Fla.	NAL	C, S, D	L-188A	Subst.	3				0	0	3			
5/17/63	Baird Bay, Alaska	WLA	P, NS, D	Beech C-18S	Dest.	7	0	0	6	0	0	1			
5/27/63	Nr. Anniston, Ala.	UAL	P, S, D	Car VIR	Minor	20	0	1	14	0	0	5			
5/28/63	Manhattan, Kan.	STA	P, MC, D	L-1049G	Dest.	70	0	1	63	0	0	6			
5/28/63	Atlantic, N.J.	AAA	P, S, D	CV-340	Subst.	41	0	0	37	0	0	4			
5/31/63	Wildwood, N.J.	USO	F	DC-6B	Subst.	5				0	0	5			

Probable Causes:

2/3/63 — Probable Cause: The continuation of an instrument approach after adequate visual reference was lost below authorized minimums. Inadequate monitoring of the instrument approach by the PAR controller was a contributing factor.

2/7/63 — Probable Cause: Failure of the flight leader of the military aircraft and the pilots of N-93123 to sight the other's aircraft in time to avoid an evasive maneuver.

2/12/63 — Under Investigation.

2/16/63 — Probable Cause: Improper handling of an emergency situation, precipitated by a mechanical malfunction, which resulted in an unsuccessful single-engine go-around. A contributing factor was the failure of Radar Approach Control to provide complete and accurate airfield data to the pilot.

3/12/63 — Probable Cause: Fatigue failure of the right main landing gear shock strut cylinder during the landing roll. Unfavorable runway condition for landing.

3/16/63 — Probable Cause: Collapse of the nose gear during the landing roll caused by inadequate maintenance and inspection. Inadequate preflight inspection.

3/18/63 — Probable Cause: An improperly executed instrument approach in turbulent air, resulting in descent below obstructing terrain.

3/25/63 — Probable Cause: Investigated by Panamanian Government.

4/2/63 — Probable Cause: Power failure resulting from fuel contamination caused by improper and inadequate fueling procedure.

4/10/63 — Probable Cause: Under Investigation.

4/18/63 — Probable Cause: The sudden encounter of momentary moderate in-flight turbulence before turbulence procedures could be completed.

5/8/63 — Probable Cause: Inadvertent movement of the cockpit landing gear control from the down position shortly before or after landing touchdown.

5/15/63 — Probable Cause: Failure of the pilots to extend the landing gear prior to landing.

5/17/63 — Probable Cause: A loss of directional control during the takeoff roll caused by unsuitable runway conditions. Inadequate flight preparation.

5/27/63 — Probable Cause: In-flight turbulence.

5/28/63 (Manhattan, Kan.) — Probable Cause: In-flight reversal of the No. 3 propeller due to a propeller power unit malfunction, resulting from improper maintenance practices and inspection procedure.

5/28/63 (Atlantic, N.J.) — Probable Cause: Material failure of the left landing gear caused by improper maintenance and inspection.

5/31/63 — Probable Cause: Premature and improper gear retraction action by the flight engineer during a go-around. Inadequate crew coordination and supervision by the pilot in command.

U.S. AIR CARRIER ACCIDENTS (ALL OPERATIONS) 1963

Date	Location	Airline	Type of Service	Airplane	Damage	Total Aboard	Passengers F	S	M/N	Crew F	S	M/N	Others F	S	M/N
6/3/63	Pacific Ocean, WSW of Annette Island, Alaska	NWA	P, MC, I	DC-7C	Dest.	101	95	0	0	6	0	0			
	Unable to determine cause.														
6/8/63	Chicago, Ill.	AAL	P, S, D	L-188	None	56	0	0	51	0	1	4			
	Probable Cause: In-flight turbulence.														
6/9/63	Fairfield, Ohio	COP	C, MC	AW-650	Subst.	3				0	0	3			
	Probable Cause: Inadvertent gear retraction by the captain during the landing roll.														
6/17/63	Baton Rouge, La.	SOU	P, S, D	M-404	Subst.	19	0	0	16	0	0	3			
	Probable Cause: Pilot misjudged level off and made improper recovery from the resultant bounced landing.														
6/23/63	North of Norfolk, Va.	EAL	P, S, I	DC-8	Minor	69	0	3	59	0	0	7			
	Probable Cause: Clear air turbulence. Failure of the pilots to initiate timely penetration procedures in an area of forecast clear-air turbulence.														
6/28/63	In-flight over Litchfield, Mich.	AAL	P, S, D	B707B	None	139	0	1	131	0	0	7			
	Probable Cause: In-flight turbulence. Failure of some passengers to comply with the crew's instructions.														
7/2/63	Rochester, N.Y.	MOH	P, S, D	M-404	Dest.	43	5	29	6	2	1	0			
	Probable Cause: A loss of control during an attempted takeoff into a severe thunderstorm.														
7/2/63	In flight nr. Bradford, Pa.	AAL	P, S, D	L-188	None	76	0	0	71	0	1	4			
	Probable Cause: In-flight turbulence associated with thunderstorm activity.														
7/8/63	Wilmington, N.C.	PAWA	P, S, I	B707-121	None	117	0	1	107	0	0	9			
	Probable Cause: Clear air turbulence. Failure of the captain to establish turbulence penetration procedures caused by his inaccurate evaluation of the reported and observed weather.														
7/9/63	Kailua, Kona, Hawaii	ALO	P, S, D	F-27	Subst.	20	0	0	18	0	0	2			
	Probable Cause: Failure of the ground crewman to assure adequate security of the ground power unit during aircraft starting.														
7/15/63	Los Angeles, Calif.	LAA	T	S-61L	Subst.	3				0	0	3			
	Probable Cause: Fatigue failure of the right landing gear forged attachment fittings.														
7/23/63	Seldovia, Alaska	COA	P, S, D	G-44	Dest.	4	0	0	2	0	0	2			
	Probable Cause: Pilot misjudged speed and distance and overshot during landing. Inadequate supervision by the check-pilot.														
7/28/63	In flight nr. Des Moines, Iowa	UAL	P, S, D	DC-8	None	56	0	1	52	0	0	3			
	Probable Cause: In-flight turbulence during passage between cloud buildups.														
7/31/63	Sheppard AFB, Wichita Falls, Tex.	AX	C, MC, D	C-40	Subst.	2				0	0	2			
	Probable Cause: Pilot failed to use adequate caution during night taxi on a poorly lighted ramp area. Unmarked obstruction.														
8/7/63	San Francisco, Calif.	PAC	P, S, D	F-27A	Subst.	18	0	1	14	0	0	3			
	Probable Cause: Failure of the ramp crew to assure the brakes were engaged on carts parked on a ramp area subjected to propeller wash.														
8/13/63	In flight, McGuire AFB, Wrightstown, N.J.	PAWA	P, MC, I	B707-321	None	169	0	0	159	0	1	9			
	Probable Cause: Aircraft encountered turbulence with inadequate opportunity to complete the turbulence preparation procedures under the existing circumstances.														
8/13/63	Indianapolis, Ind.	DAL	P, S, D	DC-6	Subst.	24	0	0	19	0	0	5			
	Probable Cause: Pilot misjudged distance and undershot during the landing approach.														
8/14/63	Nr. Great Falls, Mont.	AX	C, MC, D	C-46-F	Subst.	2				1	1	0			
	Probable Cause: The failure of the captain to effect a proper and timely assessment of a powerplant malfunction, followed by improper judgment and technique during a single-engine emergency operation.														

U.S. AIR CARRIER ACCIDENTS (ALL OPERATIONS) 1963

Date	Location	Airline	Service	Airplane	Damage	Total Aboard	Passengers F	S	M/N	Crew F	S	M/N	Others F	S	M/N
8/15/63	Republic of Panama — Under the jurisdiction of the Panamanian Government.	BNF	—	DC-7C	Subst.	52	0	0	45	0	0	7			
8/21/63	Wilkes-Barre-Scranton, Pa. — Probable Cause: Pilot misjudged level off during landing at the conclusion of an instrument approach.	EAL	P, S, D	CV-440	Subst.	10	0	0	7	0	0	3			
8/21/63	Orlando, Fla. — Probable Cause: Pilots failed to assure the landing gear was extended prior to landing. Inadequate supervision of the flight by the captain.	EAL	P, S, D	DC-8	Subst.	28	0	0	21	0	0	7			
8/23/63	Nr. Qinhagak, Alaska — Probable Cause: Fuel starvation resulting from foreign matter contamination of the fuel screen caused by inadequate maintenance and inspection.	NC	C, S, D	Pil PC6	Subst.	1				0	0	1			
8/24/63	Calgary, Canada — Under the jurisdiction of the Canadian government.	WCA	—	F-27	Dest.	16	0	2	11	0	1	2			
9/5/63	Anchorage, Alaska — Probable Cause: Hydraulic system failure caused by the fatigue failure of pressure line external ground service fitting. Malfunction of the landing gear position warning system caused by inadequate maintenance and inspection.	COA	C, NS, D	C-46	Subst.	2				0	0	2			
9/10/63	Los Angeles, Calif. — Probable Cause: Pilot of N-705PA misjudged clearance distance during taxi.	PAWA	P, S, I	B-707-331	Minor	81	0	0	69	0	0	12			
9/12/63	Nr. Egegik, Alaska — Probable Cause: Aircraft failed to become airborne in time to clear obstruction caused by drag and lack of buoyancy on the left float resulting from water in the float. Judgment of the pilot in attempting takeoff with a known aircraft discrepancy.	WEA	P, SN, D	Cessna-180	Subst.	2	0	0	1	0	0	1			
9/21/63	SE of Topeka, Kan. — Probable Cause: Unexpected in-flight turbulence.	TWA	P, S, D	B-707-131	None	68	0	0	60	0	1	7			
9/23/63	NE of Phoenix, Ariz. — Probable Cause: An abrupt evasive maneuver necessitated to avoid collision.	AAL	P, S, D	B-707-123	None	95	0	1	86	0	0	8			
9/25/63	Orlando, Fla. — Probable Cause: Failure of the defective right main tire tube during the takeoff roll, resulting in a loss of directional control.	RID	C, S, D	C-46	Subst.	2				0	0	2			
9/25/63	Las Vegas, Nev. — Probable Cause: An improperly executed approach and landing during an emergency single-engine operation resulting in an overshoot.	AX	C, MC, D	C-46-F	Subst.	2				0	0	2			
9/28/63	Nashville, Tenn. — Probable Cause: A loss of directional control during the landing roll caused by improper reversing technique.	EAL	P, S, D	DC-7	Subst.	45	0	0	40	0	0	5			
9/28/63	Los Angeles, Calif. — Probable Cause: Failure of the ground crewman to assure that the ramp was clear before releasing the aircraft for taxi.	TWA	P, S, D	B-707-131	Subst.	102	0	0	94	0	0	8			
9/29/63	Shreveport, La. — Probable Cause: An emergency wheels-up landing caused by inadequate preflight inspection and pretakeoff checks.	AFAX	P, MC, D	DC-3	Subst	31	0	0	28	0	0	3			
10/14/63	Jamaica, N.Y. — Probable Cause: Fatigue failure of the drive quill shaft due to contamination of the lubrication system in the aft transmission assembly.	NYA	P, S, D	V-107-11	Dest.	6	3	0	0	3	0	0			
10/14/63	Paris, France — Under the jurisdiction of the French Government.	TWA	—	B-707-331B	Subst.	14	0	0	7	0	0	7			
10/19/63	Los Mochis, Mex. — Under the jurisdiction of the Mexican Government.	WAL	—	L-188A	None	87	0	2	80	0	0	5			
11/1/63	Nr. Atlanta, Ga. — Probable Cause: In-flight lightning strike.	EAL	P, S, D	DC-7B	Subst.	28	0	0	23	0	0	5			
11/1/63	Atlanta, Ga. — Probable Cause: Fatigue failure of the left main landing gear wheel axle.	DAL	P, S, D	CV-440	Subst.	38	0	0	35	0	0	3			
11/6/63	Boston, Mass. — Probable Cause: In-flight engine fire. Material failure of the No. 3 low pressure compressor spacer of the No. 4 engine.	EAL	P, S, D	B-720	Subst.	38	0	0	31	0	0	7			

U.S. AIR CARRIER ACCIDENTS (ALL OPERATIONS) 1963

Date	Location	Airline	Type of Service	Airplane	Damage	Total Aboard	Passengers			Crew			Others		
							F	S	M/N	F	S	M/N	F	S	M/N
11/9/63	Nr. Houston, Tex. Under investigation.	EAL	P, S, I	DC-8	Subst.	128	0	1	120	0	1	6			
11/21/63	Seymour, Johnson AFB, North Carolina Probable Cause: A loss of directional control during parking, resulting from hydraulic system failure caused by inadequate maintenance and inspection.	COP	C, MC	AR AW-650	Subst.	3				0	0	3			
11/29/63	Morgantown, W. Va. Under investigation.	PUR	F	DC-3	Dest.	3				1	1	1			
12/2/63	Oakland, Calif. Probable Cause: Power failure resulting in metal contamination of the fuel control unit caused by inadequate maintenance and inspection.	SOA	P, S, D	S-62A	Subst.	11	0	0	10	0	0	1			
12/4/63	Lakeland, Fla. Probable Cause: In-flight turbulence. Failure of the captain to use earlier turbulence precautions for cabin occupants over an area of forecast turbulence.	EAL	P, S, I	DC-8	None	70	0	1	62	0	0	7			
12/4/63	Kodiak, Alaska Probable Cause: Pilot attempted takeoff from terrain which was unsuitable under existing conditions. Inadequate flight preparation for a company practice with insufficient safety consideration.	KOAX	F	PA-18-150	Subst.	1				0	0	1			
12/7/63	Nederland, Colorado Under investigation.	ZATX	C, MC	C-46	Dest.	3	1	0	0	2	0	0			
12/8/63	Elkton, Md. Probable Cause: Lightning induced ignition of the fuel air mixture in the No. 1 reserve fuel tank with resultant explosive disintegration of the left outer wing and loss of control.	PAWA	P, S, I	B-707	Dest.	81	73	0	0	8	0	0			
12/11/63	Kalispell, Mont. Probable Cause: Pilot misjudged level off and made improper recovery from the resultant bounced landing. Inadequate supervision by the captain.	WCA	P, S, D	DC-3	Subst.	6	0	0	3	0	0	3			
12/12/63	New Orleans, La. Probable Cause: Engine failure caused by material failure of the compressor rotor disk spacer assembly. Inadequate maintenance and inspection.	EAL	P, S, D	B-720-025	Subst.	16	0	0	10	0	0	6			
12/17/63	Los Angeles, Calif. Probable Cause: The failure of the pilot to maintain a positive rate of climb and the premature retraction of the landing gear during a go-around in fog conditions.	WAL	P, S, D	DC-6B	Subst.	46	0	0	40	0	0	6			

U.S. AIR CARRIER ACCIDENTS (ALL OPERATIONS) 1964

Date	Location	Airline	Type of Service	Airplane	Damage	Total Aboard	Passengers			Crew			Others		
1/1/64	Boston, Mass. Probable Cause: Pilot misjudged speed and distance, resulting in an overshoot during landing. Reduced braking caused by unfavorable surface conditions.	TWA	P, S, D	CV-880	Subst.	66	0	0	58	0	0	8			
1/1/64	Hill AFB, Utah Probable Cause: Fatigue failure of the right main landing gear axle elbow.	AX	C, MC, D	C-46A	Subst.	3				0	0	3			
1/5/64	Miami, Fla. Probable Cause: Fuel explosion caused by a fuel leak in the auxiliary fuel tank ignited by the right engine exhaust flame.	PAWA	T	DC-3A	Subst.	2				0	0	2			
1/11/64	St. Louis, Mo. Probable Cause: Malfunction of the landing gear caused by inadequate security of the nose gear steerage engaging lock. Inadequate landing gear warning indication system.	OZA	F	F-27	Subst.	2				0	0	2			
1/13/64	Nr. Asheville, N.C. Probable Cause: Failure of the passenger to comply with the fasten seat belt instruction.	UAL	P, S, D	Vis 745D	None	23	0	0	20	0	1	2			
1/20/64	Petersburg, Alaska Probable Cause: Pilot failed to see and avoid an obstruction during flight at an unwarranted low altitude.	ACE	P, S, D	G-21A	Subst.	3	0	0	2	0	0	1			
1/21/64	Karluk, Kodiak Isl., Alaska Probable Cause: Pilot misjudged speed and distance and undershot during the approach for landing.	KOAX	P, S, D	G-44	Subst.	4	0	0	3	0	0	1			

U.S. AIR CARRIER ACCIDENTS (ALL OPERATIONS) 1964

Date	Location	Airline	Type of Service	Type of Airplane	Damage	Total Aboard	Passengers F	Passengers S	Passengers M/N	Crew F	Crew S	Crew M/N	Others F	Others S	Others M/N
2/12/64	Huntsville, Ala.	SOU	P, S, D	DC-3	None	29	0	1	25	0	0	3			
2/12/64	Las Vegas, Nev.	BAL	P, S, D	F-27A	Subst.	34	0	0	31	0	0	3			
2/13/64	Hilo, Hawaii	HAL	P, S, D	CV-440	Subst.	40	0	3	34	0	0	3			
2/21/64	Denver, Colo.	ZATX	C, MC, D	C-46A	Subst.	3				0	0	3			
2/24/64	Miami, Fla.	NWA	P, S, D	B-720B	Subst.	40	0	0	33	0	0	7			
2/25/64	New Orleans, La.	EAL	P, S, D	DC-8	Dest.	58	51	0	0	7	0	0			
2/29/64	Binghampton, N.Y.	MOA	P, S, D	M-404	Subst.	44	0	0	41	0	0	3			
3/4/64	Tupelo, Miss.	SOU	P, S, D	DC-3	Subst.	5	0	0	2	0	0	3			
3/9/64	Boston, Mass.	TWA	P, S, D	L-749	Subst.	14	0	0	9	0	0	5			
3/10/64	Boston, Mass.	SLIX	C, S, D	DC-4	Dest.	3				3	0	0			
3/12/64	Miles City, Montana	FAL	P, S, D	DC-3C	Dest.	5	2	0	0	3	0	0			
3/17/64	Nr. Billings, Mont.	NWA	P, S, D	B-720B	None	41	0	1	33	0	1	6			
3/22/64	E. of Umiat, Alaska	WLA	P, NS, D	DHC-2	Subst.	2	0	0	1	0	0	1			
3/26/64	Nr. Tampa, Fla.	DAL	P, S, D	CV-880	Minor	93	0	1	86	0	0	6			
4/6/64	Nr. Bull River, Alaska	WLA	P, NS, D	Cessna 185	Subst.	3	0	0	2	0	0	1			
4/7/64	Jamaica, N.Y.	PAWA	P, S, I	B-707	Subst.	145	0	15	121	0	1	8			
4/10/64	Montpelier, Vt.	NEA	P, S, D	DC-3A	Subst.	20	0	0	16	0	0	4			

Probable Causes:

2/12/64 Huntsville, Ala. — Probable Cause: Release of the passengers' seat belts in turbulence for an undetermined reason.

2/12/64 Las Vegas, Nev. — Probable Cause: Failure of the pilots to discontinue an improperly planned and executed landing, resulting in an overshoot. Inadequate supervision by the captain.

2/13/64 Hilo, Hawaii — Probable Cause: Failure of the pilot to execute a go-around during a landing overshoot under adverse weather and runway landing conditions. Ineffective braking due to aquaplaning during the landing roll.

2/21/64 Denver, Colo. — Probable Cause: Failure of the crew to properly utilize the emergency landing gear extension system. Failure of the normal hydraulic system caused by material failure of the right engine hydraulic pressure line.

2/24/64 Miami, Fla. — Probable Cause: Improper manufacture of the third stage nozzle guide vane inner ring and inadequate maintenance and inspection during engine overhaul.

2/25/64 New Orleans, La. — Probable Cause: The degredation on aircraft stability characteristics in turbulence, because of abnormal longitudinal trim component positions.

2/29/64 Binghampton, N.Y. — Probable Cause: Captain inadvertently retracted his landing gear during the landing roll.

3/4/64 Tupelo, Miss. — Probable Cause: Improper use of controls during taxi under adverse wind conditions. Judgment of the pilot in initiating and dispatch for releasing flight in existing conditions.

3/9/64 Boston, Mass. — Probable Cause: Stress corrosion and fatigue failure of the nose gear actuating strut piston rod end clevis. Inadequate manufacture and quality control.

3/10/64 Boston, Mass. — Probable Cause: Loss of balancing forces on the horizontal surface of the empennage of the aircraft, due to ice accretion, causing the aircraft to pitch nosedown at an altitude too low to effect recovery.

3/12/64 Miles City, Montana — Probable Cause: Descent below obstructing terrain, for reasons undeterminable, during an instrument approach in adverse weather conditions.

3/17/64 Nr. Billings, Mont. — Probable Cause: In-flight clear air turbulence.

3/22/64 E. of Umiat, Alaska — Probable Cause: Pilot attempted take-off from terrain which was unsuitable under existing conditions.

3/26/64 Nr. Tampa, Fla. — Probable Cause: Inadequate in-flight turbulence procedures by the pilot in an area of known potential turbulence.

4/6/64 Nr. Bull River, Alaska — Probable Cause: Pilot attempted take-off from terrain which was unsuitable under existing conditions.

4/7/64 Jamaica, N.Y. — Probable Cause: Captain's deviation from the glide slope during an ILS approach, resulting in a touchdown on the runway at a point and speed, which precluded stopping the aircraft on the remaining runway.

4/10/64 Montpelier, Vt. — Probable Cause: A loss of directional control caused by improper use of power and flight controls during a cross-wind take-off. Inadequate supervision by the captain.

U.S. AIR CARRIER ACCIDENTS (ALL OPERATIONS) 1964

Date	Location	Airline	Type of Service	Airplane	Damage	Total Aboard	Passengers F	S	M/N	Crew F	S	M/N	Others F	S	M
4/11/64	San Jose, Costa Rica	PAWA	—		DC-6B	Subst.	25	0	0	20	0	1	4			
	Probable Cause: The investigation and determination are under the jurisdiction of the Government of Costa Rica, in accordance with Annex 13 to the Convention of International Civil Aviation.																
4/17/64	Nr. Elim, Alaska	WLA	P, S, D	Cessna 185	Dest.	2	1	0	0	1	0	0				
	Probable Cause: Pilot attempted continual visual flight in adverse weather including whiteout conditions, resulting in a loss of control. Inadequate weather briefing.																
4/24/64	Cleveland, Ohio	NWA	P, S, D	L-188	Subst.	84	0	6	71	0	0	7				
	Probable Cause: Malfunction of the landing gear retraction/extension control lever assembly during the landing roll caused by inadequate maintenance and repair.																
5/4/64	Rochester, N.Y.	UAL	P, S, D	DC-6B	Subst.	29	0	0	24	0	0	5				
	Probable Cause: Malfunction of the nose gear down latch assembly, resulting from improper rigging caused by inadequate maintenance and inspection.																
5/7/64	Nr. San Ramon, Calif.	PAC	P, S, D	F-27	Dest.	44	41	0	0	3	0	0				
	Probable Cause: The shooting of the captain and copilot by a passenger during flight.																
5/8/64	Anaheim, Calif.	LAA	P, S, D	S-61L	Subst.	17	0	0	14	0	0	3				
	Probable Cause: Pilot misjudged distance during landing.																
5/12/64	Chantilly, Va.	UAL	T	Vis 745D	Subst.	3				0	0	3				
	Probable Cause: Pilot failed to extend the landing gear for landing. Inadequate use of the landing check-list.																
5/29/64	Paris, France	TWA	—	B-707-331	Subst.	103	0	0	89	0	0	14				
	Probable Cause: The investigation and determination are under the jurisdiction of the Government of France, in accordance with Annex 13 to the Convention on International Civil Aviation.																
6/5/64	Flushing, N.Y.	NEA	P, S, D	DC-6B	Subst.	43	0	0	39	0	0	4				
	Probable Cause: The failure of the captain properly to plan and execute the final approach.																
6/23/64	Togiak, Alaska	WEA	P, NS, D	Cessna 180-C	Subst.	3	0	0	2	0	1	0				
	Probable Cause: Pilot failed to assure the landing area was clear prior to landing.																
6/30/64	Jamaica, N.Y.	NAL	P, S, D	DC-8	Subst.	71	0	0	64	0	0	7				
	Probable Cause: Inadequate coordination between ground and flight crews during parking. Inadequate parking spaces.																
7/1/64	Nr. Allentown, Pa.	TWA	P, S, D	CV-880	None	45	0	0	38	0	1	6				
	Probable Cause: In-flight turbulence. Failure of the stewardess to comply with company procedures.																
7/1/64	Jamaica, N.Y.	AAL	P, S, D	B-720B	Subst.	12	0	0	5	0	0	7				
	Probable Cause: Failure of the captain to discontinue the landing approach under conditions of heavy precipitation and reduced visibility, resulting in improper alignment of the aircraft at touchdown and subsequent loss of directional control.																
7/8/64	Nr. Knoxville, Tenn.	UAL	P, S, D	Car	None	54	1	0	48	0	0	5				
	Probable Cause: Failure of the aircraft seat belts to adequately restrain passengers during turbulence for an undetermined reason. Severe turbulence.																
7/9/64	Nr. Parrottsville, Tenn.	UAL	—	Vis 745D	Dest.	39	35	0	0	4	0	0				
	Probable Cause: An uncontrollable inflight fire of undetermined origin, in the fuselage, which resulted in a loss of control of the aircraft.																
7/12/64	Nr. Kotzebue, Alaska	WLA	P, NS, D	Cessna 185	Subst.	4	0	0	3	0	0	1				
	Probable Cause: Pilot failed to obtain adequate airspeed for take-off.																
7/12/64	Ruby Creek, Alaska	WLA	C, NS, D	Pil PC-6A	Subst.	2				0	0	2				
	Probable Cause: A loss of directional control caused by improper use of brakes, flight, and propeller controls during the landing roll. Inadequate supervision by the pilot in command.																
7/15/64	New York, N.Y.	EAL	P, S, D	L-1049C	None	20	0	0	15	0	1	4				
	Probable Cause: Sudden spontaneous action of the stewardess caused by the cabin door action with which she was unfamiliar.																

U.S. AIR CARRIER ACCIDENTS (ALL OPERATIONS) 1964

Date	Location	Airline	Type of Service	Airplane	Damage	Total Aboard	Passengers F	S	M/N	Crew F	S	M/N	Others F	S	M/N
7/16/64	Richmond, Va.	EAL	P, S, D	DC-7B	Subst.	76	0	0	71	0	0	5			
	Probable Cause: Pilot misjudged altitude and distance and undershot during landing.														
7/17/64	Cordova, Alaska	COA	P, S, D	G-44	Subst.	8	0	0	1	0	0	1			
	Probable Cause: Pilot failed to extend the landing gear prior to landing.														
7/20/64	Charlotte, N.C.	EAL	P, S, D	DC-7	Subst.	57	0	0	52	0	0	5			
	Probable Cause: Improper reversing technique, resulting in the use of excessive directional corrective forces during which the aircraft struck an unsuitable runway condition. Unsuitable runway condition, resulting from inadequate runway maintenance. Inadequate supervision by the captain.														
7/20/64	Pueblo, Colo.	CEN	P, S, D	DC-3	None	14	0	0	11	0	1	2			
	Probable Cause: In-flight turbulence.														
7/24/64	Nr. Gainesville, Fla.	EAL	P, S, I	DC-8	None	137	0	1	129	0	0	7			
	Probable Cause: Failure of the passenger to comply with instructions to fasten seat belts. In-flight turbulence.														
8/26/64	Kansas City, Mo.	TWA	P, S, D	B-707-331C	Subst.	138	0	0	130	0	0	8			
	Probable Cause: Pilot misjudged distance and undershot during landing.														
8/26/64	Osceola, Mich.	ZATX	C, MC, D	AW-650	Subst.	3				0	0	3			
	Probable Cause: Premature lift-off for an undetermined reason, resulting in an aborted wheels-up landing.														
9/6/64	New York, N.Y.	NYA	TF		V-107	Subst.	2				0	0	2			
	Probable Cause: Pilot misjudged clearance distance during taxi without proper assistance.														
9/7/64	Nr. Minneapolis, Minn.	NWA	P, S, D	B-720	Minor	92	0	1	84	0	1	6			
	Probable Cause: In-flight turbulence.														
9/14/64	Farmington, N.M.	FAL	P, S, D	CV-440	Subst.	23	0	0	20	0	0	3			
	Probable Cause: Pilot misjudged level off and made improper recovery from the resulting bounced landing. Sharply reduced visibility caused by heavy rain at a critical phase during landing.														
9/22/64	San Juan, P.R.	CAR	P, S, D	DC-3	Subst.	2				0	0	2			
	Probable Cause: Premature lift-off during take-off caused by inadequate before-starting and pre-take-off checks.														
9/22/64	Sacramento, Calif.	WAL	P, S, D	B-720	Subst.	55	0	0	48	0	0	7			
	Probable Cause: Pilot misjudged speed, distance, and altitude, resulting in an undershoot and hand landing.														
9/22/64	Nr. Springfield, Va.	UAL	P, S, D	Vis	None	42	0	0	38	0	2	2			
	Probable Cause: Failure of the Air Traffic Control Facility to provide adequate separation between conflicting IFR traffic.														
9/23/64	San Juan, P.R.	EAL	P, S, I	DC-8	None	99	0	0	92	0	0	7	1	0	0
	Probable Cause: Failure of the ground crewmen to use adequate caution and to follow existing procedures.														
10/2/64	Chicagof Island, Alaska	ACL	C, S, D	CV-285ACF	Dest.	3				1	1	1			
	Probable Cause: Pilot misjudged level off and made improper recovery from the resultant bounced landing. Inadequate flight supervision by the pilot-in-command.														
10/10/64	Charleston, S.C.	COP	C, NS, MC	C-46	Subst.	2				0	0	2			
	Probable Cause: Engine failure and fire caused by material failure of the No. 11 cylinder.														
10/25/64	Rock Spgs., Wyo.	FAL	P, S, D	CV-340-48	Subst.	27	0	0	24	0	0	3			
	Probable Cause: Pilot misjudged and made improper level-off during landing. Inadequate supervision by the captain.														
10/30/64	Pittsburgh, Pa.	ZATX	F	C-46F	Subst.	2				0	0	2			
	Probable Cause: Failure of the right main landing gear to fully extend and lock during the extension time prior to landing. Malfunction of the position gear warning system, resulting in a false safe-for-landing indication.														
10/31/64	Joliet, Ill.	CHA	C, NS, D	S-58C	None	2	0	0	2	0	1	1			
	Probable Cause: Pilot misjudged height and position caused by inadequate visual reference during an inherently hazardous operation.														
11/5/64	San Francisco, Calif.	UAL	P, S, I	B-720	Subst.	94	0	0	87	0	0	7			
	Probable Cause: Failure of the nose gear normal and emergency extension system caused by the fatigue failure of nose gear drag brace lock and rod attach bolt.														

U.S. AIR CARRIER ACCIDENTS (ALL OPERATIONS) 1964

Date	Location	Airline	Service	Airplane	Damage	Total Aboard	Passengers F	S	M/N	Crew F	S	M/N	Others F	S	M/N
11/9/64	Nr. Chicago, Ill.	TWA	P, S, D	CV-880	None	50	0	0	43	0	2	5			
	Probable Cause: An evasive maneuver to avoid an apparent collision potential.														
11/12/64	Nashville, Tenn.	AAL	P, S, D	B-707	Subst.	66	0	0	59	0	0	7			
	Probable Cause: Stress and fatigue failure of the Nos. 5 and 6 axle sections of the left main landing gear axle assemblies.														
11/12/64	Detroit, Mich.	FTLX	C, S, D	Can CL-44	Subst.	3				0	0	3			
	Probable Cause: Fatigue failure of the left main landing gear uplock actuating cylinder.														
11/12/64	Cape Alitak, Alaska	KOAX	P, S, D	G-44	Subst.	5	0	0	4	0	0	1			
	Probable Cause: Aircraft struck a submerged object during take-off.														
11/14/64	Wichita, Kans.	TWA	P, S, D	L749A	Minor	20	0	0	15	0	0	5			
	Probable Cause: Extreme in-flight turbulence during an instrument landing approach in frontal weather conditions.														
11/15/64	Las Vegas, Nev.	BAL	P, S, D	F-27	Dest.	29	26	0	0	3	0	0			
	Probable Cause: Misinterpretation of the approach chart by the captain which resulted in a premature descent below obstructing terrain.														
11/19/64	Norfolk, Va.	SLIX	C, S, D	DC-4	Subst.	2				0	0	2			
	Probable Cause: Fatigue failure of the right nosewheel yoke and fitting.														
11/19/64	Gwinn, Mich.	ZATX	C, MC, D	AW-650	Subst.	3				0	0	3			
	Probable Cause: Failure of the electric spraymat element in the left horizontal stabilizer de-icer unit, resulting in an in-flight fire.														
11/20/64	Inkster, Mich.	ZATX	C, NS, D	C-46A	Dest.	2				0	0	2			
	Probable Cause: A loss of lift during take-off, resulting from airframe icing caused by inadequate de-icing and preflight inspection.														
11/23/64	Rome, Italy	TWA	P, S, I	B707-331	Dest.	73	45	17	0	5	0	6			
	Probable Cause: The investigation and determination are under the jurisdiction of the Government of Italy, in accordance with Annex 13 to the Convention on International Civil Aviation.														
11/24/64	Baton Rouge, La.	DAL	C, S, D	C-46	Subst.	2				0	0	2			
	Probable Cause: Failure of the captain to execute a go-around during a landing overshoot under existing unfavorable wind and adverse runway conditions. Ineffective braking due to hydroplaning.														
11/25/64	Covington, Ky.	ZATX	C, NS, D	C-46	Subst.	2				0	0	2			
	Probable Cause: Collapse of the right landing gear during landing caused by the deteriorated condition of the right gear side bushing of improper metal composition. Malfunction of the landing gear position warning system caused by inadequate maintenance and inspection.														
11/28/64	Nr. Hughes, Alaska	WLA	P, S, D	Pil PC-6A	Subst.	5	0	0	4	0	0	1			
	Probable Cause: Accumulation of water in the strut tube, resulting in sudden extension of the strut from a frozen compressed position.														
12/22/64	Seldovia, Alaska	COA	P, S, D	Cessna 185	Subst.	2	0	0	1	0	0	1			
	Probable Cause: Pilot failed to adequately compensate for unfavorable wind conditions, resulting in a loss of directional control during landing. Unfavorable natural and physical environment of the airport.														
12/24/64	San Francisco, Calif.	FTLX	C, S, D	L-1049	Dest.	3				3	0	0			
	Probable Cause: The pilot, for undetermined reasons, deviated from departure course into an area of rising terrain where downdraft activity and turbulence affected the climb capability of the aircraft sufficiently to prevent terrain clearance.														
12/30/64	Saugus, Calif.	UAL	P, S, D	CV-340	Subst.	47	0	0	43	0	0	4			
	Probable Cause: Fuel starvation induced power failure of both engines caused by mismanagement of the fuel system and inattention to fuel supply.														
12/30/64	Detroit, Mich.	ZATX	C, NS, D	C-46A	Dest.	4				4	0	0			
	Probable Cause: Loss of control during night instrument approach in adverse weather for an undetermined reason.														

U.S. AIR CARRIER ACCIDENTS (ALL OPERATIONS) 1965

Some of the 1965 accident investigations are not completed, so the format of this summary has been modified.

Date	Location	Airline	Type of Service	Airplane	Damage	Total Aboard	Reported Type of Accident
1/5/65	St. Louis, Mo.	ZATX	C, D	C-46F	Subst.	2	Struck semi-trailer during taxi.
1/8/65	Tulsa, Okla.	CEN	P, S, D	CV-240	Subst.	12	Wheels-up landing.
1/8/65	San Juan, P.R.	EAL	P, S, I	DC-8	Subst.	19	Right gear axle broke during taxi.
1/18/65	Bradley, Conn.	MOH	P, S, D	CV-440	None	13	Passenger injured during air maneuver.
1/21/65	Lancaster, Pa.	AAA	P, S, D	CV-440	Subst.	26	Ran off end of runway during landing.
1/21/65	Staunton, Va.	PAI	P, S, D	M-404	Subst.	28	Left gear retracted during landing.
1/23/65	Nr. Chicago Hgts., Ill.	NWA	P, S, D	B-720B	None	49	In-flight turbulence
1/24/65	Nr. Allentown, Pa.	UAL	P, S, D	Car	None	31	In-flight turbulence.
1/31/65	Nr. Bermuda Is.	PAWA	P, S, I	B-707	None	77	In-flight turbulence.
2/8/65	Atlanta, Ga.	ZATX	C, D	C-46	Subst.	4	Left gear retracted during landing.
2/8/65	Atlantic Ocean, Nr. Kennedy Int'l., New York, N.Y.	EAL	P, S, D	DC-7B	Dest.	84	Crashed shortly after take-off. Fatalities: 84.
2/17/65	Los Angeles, Calif.	TWA	P, S, D	B-707	Minor	15	Struck parked aircraft during taxi.
2/22/65	Nr. Kennedy Int'l., N.Y.	MOH	P, S, D	CV-240	None	47	Stewardess injured during air maneuver.
3/2/65	Wilmington, N.C.	NEA	P, S, D	CV-880	None	105	In-flight turbulence.
3/4/65	Fort Wayne, Ind.	UAL	P, S, D	DC-6B	Subst.	58	Nose gear collapsed during landing.
3/5/65	Kennedy Int'l., N.Y.	EAL	P, S, I	DC-8	Subst.	84	Hard landing, No. 4 engine separated during landing roll.
3/14/65	Ypsilanti, Mich.	UAL	P, S, D	Car	Subst.	55	Left engine disintegrated during take-off roll.
3/17/65	Kansas City, Mo.	TWA	P, S, D	B727	Subst.	97	Left wing struck runway during landing.
3/19/65	Houston, Tex.	BNF	P, S, D	B-720	Subst.	61	Hard landing, damaging fuselage and nose gear.
3/25/65	Albany, N.Y.	MOH	P, S, D	CV-440	Subst.	43	Fire in cargo compartment during taxi.
3/26/65	Saigon, S. Viet Nam	PAWA	P, MC, I	B-707/321	Subst.	170	Dragged No. 4 engine pod during landing.
3/28/65	Prescott, Ariz.	BAL	P, S, D	F-27A	None	41	In-flight turbulence.
4/1/65	16 mi. SE of Julian, Calif.	BAL	P, S, D	F-27A	None	43	In-flight turbulence.
4/15/65	4 mi. NE of Oakland, Calif.	SFA	Flt. Check	S-62	Dest.	2	Ditched after engine malfunction.
4/16/65	Las Vegas, Nev.	BAL	T	F-27A	Subst.	2	Groundlooped during takeoff.
4/16/65	San Francisco, Calif.	SFA	P, S, D	S-62	Dest.	2	Forced landing after engine malfunction.
4/19/65	Nr. Talahassee, Fla.	EAL	P, S, D	L-188	None	58	In-flight turbulence.
4/19/65	English Bay, Alaska	COA	P, S, D	Cessna 180	Subst.	3	Hard landing.
4/23/65	Merida, Mexico	PAWA	P, S, I	B-707/100B	Subst.	102	Damaged nose gear during landing.
4/23/65	Mt. Ranier, Wash.	AX	C, MC, D	DC-6A	Dest.	5	Crashed on mountain enroute. Fatalities: 5.
4/27/65	Ponce, P.R.	CBA	P, S, I	CV-340	Subst.	44	Aircraft damaged during landing.
5/3/65	Los Angeles, Calif.	CAL	P, S, D	B-720B	Subst.	22	No. 1 and 2 engines failed during takeoff.
5/4/65	Nr. Chicago, Ill.	TWA	P, S, D	CV-880	None	57	In-flight turbulence.
5/5/65	San Francisco, Calif.	SFA	F	S-62A	Subst.	2	Tail rotor struck truck during taxi.
5/9/65	Dyess AFB, Tex.	AAL	P, S, D	B-707/123	Subst.	95	Hail damage enroute at 26,000 feet.
5/11/65	El Paso, Tex.	AAL	P, S, D	B-707/100	Subst.	126	Partial failure of left gear during takeoff.
5/18/65	Nobnoster, Mo.	AX	C, MC, D	DC-6A	Dest.	3	Struck trees during final approach.
5/29/65	Nikolski, Alaska	RAA	P, S, D	DC-3	Subst.	5	Groundlooped during takeoff.
6/9/65	San Francisco, Calif.	NAL	P, S, D	DC-8	Subst.	78	No. 1 engine fire after takeoff.
6/28/65	San Francisco, Calif.	PAWA	P, S, D	B-707/321B	Subst.	153	Explosive fire and separation in right outboard wing after takeoff.
7/1/65	Kansas City, Mo.	CAL	P, S, D	B-707/124	Subst.	65	Overshot and struck mound during landing.
7/5/65	Texarkana, Ark.	AAL	P, S, D	B-707/123B	Subst.	Unknown	Hail damage enroute at 31,000 feet.
7/6/65	Nr. Omaha, Neb.	TWA	P, S, D	B-707/131	None	52	In-flight turbulence.
7/17/65	Nr. San Jose, Calif.	ZATX	C, MC, D	DC-6A	Subst.	4	No. 3 engine cowl separated during flight.

U.S. AIR CARRIER ACCIDENTS (ALL OPERATIONS) 1965

Some of the 1965 accident investigations are not completed, so the format of this summary has been modified.

Date	Location	Airline	Type of Service	Airplane	Damage	Total Aboard	Reported Type of Accident
7/23/65	Nr. Williamsport, Pa.	AAA	P, S, D	CV-440	Dest.	40	Crashed shortly after takeoff.
8/2/65	Newport, Vt.	NEA	P, S, D	DC-3	None	8	In-flight turbulence.
8/12/65	Nr. Battle Mt., Nev.	WAL	P, S, D	L-188A	None	94	In-flight turbulence.
8/12/65	Nr. Salem, Ore.	ZATX	C, MC, D	C-46A	Subst.	2	In-flight turbulence.
8/15/65	Boston, Mass.	UAL	F	DC-6A	Subst.	3	Nose gear malfunction during landing.
8/16/65	Lake Michigan, Nr. Chicago, Ill.	UAL	P, S, D	B-727	Dest.	30	Crashed during descent for landing. Fatalities: 30.
8/17/65	Nr. Leavenworth, Kan.	CAL	P, S, D	B-720B	None	110	Evasive maneuver during enroute descent.
8/23/65	Bettles, Alaska	WLA	P, S, D	CS-185	Subst.	4	Struck fuel drum during taxi after landing.
8/31/65	Atlanta, Ga.	ZATX	C, D	C-46	Subst.	2	Left landing gear retracted during landing roll.
9/1/65	Utica, N.Y.	MOH	P, S, D	BAC-111	Subst.	31	Nose gear retracted during landing roll.
9/4/65	Lake Tustumena, Alaska	COA	P, S, D	Aer 60	Dest.	5	Collided with water during flight. Fatalities: 4.
9/11/65	Mexico City, Mex.	BNF	P, S, I	B-720	Subst.	127	Nose gear strut failed.
9/13/65	Kansas City, Mo.	TWA	T	CV-880	Dest.	4	Crashed and burned after take-off.
9/13/65	Dover AFB, Del.	ZATX	C, MC, D	C-46	Subst.	3	Loss of power on take-off.
9/14/65	Stevens Pt., Wisc.	NOR	P, S, D	DC-3	Subst.	8	Struck trees during VOR approach to airport.
9/14/65	McCarthy, Alaska	COA	C, NS, D	DC-3	Subst.	4	Left tire deflated during landing.
9/17/65	Montserrat Is., British W.I.	PAWA	P, S, I	B-707	Dest.	30	Crashed enroute. Fatalities: 30.
9/19/65	Ardmore, Okla.	AFAX	F	L-049	Subst.	3	Overshot during landing.
9/19/65	San Jose, Calif.	PAC	P, S, D	M-404	None	7	Prop-to-person accident.
10/10/65	Selawik, Alaska	WLA	P, S, D	PP-8C-6A	Subst.	6	Collided with ditch during landing.
10/14/65	Piqua, Ohio	ZATX	C, MC, D	AW-650	Subst.	3	Forced landing on highway enroute.
10/15/65	San Diego, Calif. NAS	UAL	P, CT, D	DC-8	Subst.	117	Collided with another aircraft during taxi.
10/16/65	Charlotte, N.C.	EAL	P, S, D	DC-7	Subst.	57	Right landing gear failed during landing.
10/17/65	Huntsville, Ala.	UAL	P, S, D	DC-6	Subst.	16	Nose wheel collapsed during take-off roll.
10/17/65	Glenwood Spgs., Colo.	CAL	P, S, D	B-707/ 320C	None	114	In-flight turbulence.
11/8/65	College Station, Tex.	TTA	P, S, D	CV-240	Subst.	10	Groundlooped during landing.
11/8/65	Nr. Cincinnati, Ohio	AAL	P, S, D	B-727	Dest.	62	Crashed during approach for landing. Fatalities: 58.
11/11/65	Salt Lake City, Utah	UAL	P, S, D	B-727	Dest.	91	Crashed on runway during landing. Fatalities: 43.
11/15/65	Arctic Village, Alaska	WLA	C, S, D	DHC-2	Subst.	1	Hard landing on frozen river.
11/24/65	Nr. Los Gatos, Calif.	PAC	P, S, D	F-27	Subst.	33	In-flight lightning strike (6000 feet)
12/1/65	Hoquiam, Wash.	WCA	P, S, D	DC-3	Subst.	13	Overshot runway.
12/4/65	North Salem, N.Y.	EAL	P, S, D	L-1049	Dest.	54	Mid-air collision. Fatalities: 4.
		TWA	P, S, D	B-707	Subst.	58	
12/7/65	Tampa, Fla.	NAL	P, S, D	B-727	Subst	60	No. 1 engine disintegrated on take-off. Take-off aborted.
12/8/65	Yuma, Ariz.	BAL	P, S, D	F-27	Subst.	17	Gear collapsed during landing.
12/15/65	NE of Alamosa, Colo.	FTLX	C, S, D	L-1049H	Dest.	3	Crashed enroute. Fatalities: 3.
12/16/65	Detroit, Mich.	ZATX	C, D	C-46	None		Prop-to-person accident. Fatalities: 1.
12/20/65	Bethel, Alaska	NCA	P, S, D	Cessna 180	Subst.	2	Stalled after takeoff (frost on wings).
12/20/65	Bethel, Alaska	NCA	P, S, D	G-7-3	Subst.	9	Stalled after takeoff (frost on wings).
12/22/65	NW of San Diego, Calif.	UAL	P, S, D	DC-8	None	10	In-flight turbulence.

9081 ▬